ORIGINAL WRITING

from

IRELAND'S OWN

2011

ORIGINAL WRITING

© 2011 VARIOUS

Cover photo of Croagh Patrick, County Mayo by Steven Weekes

978-1-908477-36-1

A CIP catalogue for this book is available from the National Library.

Published by ORIGINAL WRITING LTD., Dublin, 2011.

Printed by CLONDALKIN GROUP, Dublin 17.

INTRODUCTION

Ireland's Own, in conjunction with Original Writing, is delighted to bring to readers this second Athology of the winners and other highly commended entries in our annual writing competitions for 2010. The success of our initial effort last year, which was very well received, has encouraged us to publish this second selection which we feel sure will be equally enjoyed.

Ireland's Own has always tried to encourage the idea of writing among ordinary people and we are one of the few outlets for budding writers of both factual articles and fiction. Apart from our regular corps of professional and part-time contributors, we also receive a great many unsolicited submissions every week, many of them of a very good standard. We are constantly reminded of the great hunger there is out there among people who desire to commit their ideas to print. Writing has never been so popular and we do try to be sympathetic and encouraging in our approach, though we are only in a position to use a small fraction of the work submitted.

We have been running our Annual Short Stories and Memories Writing Competitions for many years, and they attract a great and high-standard response. For the past four years we have been supported in this by the self-publishing company, Original Writing, from Dublin, and their backing is greatly appreciated and our partnership with them has again made this anthology possible.

We congratulate the three overall category winners, the other prizewinners and the more than thirty other writers included. We thank them all for their help and co-operation with this project. We also compliment everybody else who entered.

Legendary broadcaster Donncha O Dulaing has always been a great friend to Ireland's Own; we thank him for his ongoing support and for his generous foreword to this book; we also thank former Ireland's Own editors, Gerry Breen and Margaret

Galvin, for all their help with the annual competitions. A special word of thanks to Martin Delany, Garrett Bonner, Steven Weekes and all the crew at Original Writing for their expertise, patience and assistance.

Inclusion in this anthology is a significant step for all the writers involved; we meet a few old friends in this second collection, but there are a few others who are being published in a book for the first time and it is very special for them in particular. We wish them all future success if they pursue their writing ambitions. Ireland's Own is happy to have played a part in helping you along the way.

Phil Murphy, Monthly Editor
Sean Nolan, Weekly Editor
Ireland's Own.

FOREWORD *by Donncha O Dulaing*

'The flower of art,' said Henry James, 'blooms only where the soul is deep.'

He would certainly have approved of the 'Ireland's Own Anthology of Original Writing, Volume Two', a wonderful and well produced collection from the magazine's annual writing competitions for 2010, which is following on from the success of last year's initial effort.

I am thrilled to be asked to write this foreword. Indeed, I feel happier than most in that my life, traditions and professional life brings me in the very doorstep of Ireland's favourite magazine.

My links with Ireland's Own began in far-off days in my home town of Doneraile, Co. Cork, where I first encountered this fountain of stories, essays, jokes and Irishness in Titridge's shop. It has continued right through to my current Failte Isteach life, and to my personal life when my last moments awake every night are spent reading the Ireland's Own.

So, when Phil Murphy, Editor of Ireland's Own and compiler of this book, asked me to write these few words, my delight was indescribable.

I congratulate all of you whose contributions are included in this book and I marvel at your skill and creativity. It is wonderful to have made it between these covers, but I trust this is just a step on the road to even greater acclaim and success for you. Kitty the Hare would have spoken about you in the past, never minding her creator, Victor O'D. Power.

Maybe I've just hit the nail on the head, and Phil and his colleagues have dipped even deeper than they think into the fertile soil of Ireland's Own and proved, if needed, that Henry James was right.

Finally, before I leave you in this foreword, I must tell you that only recently I sat in Canon Sheehan's old garden in Doneraile and a surge of boyhood memories engulfed me ... and from the heart of echoes came the world of Failte Isteach, a brief TV journey to the world of of RTE's popular 'Nationwide' programme, where 'Failte' was recently featured, accompanied by an old edition of Ireland's Own on my desk, and P.J. Murrihy's song 'Life in the old dog yet!' on the turntable. This is it!

Beannaím   sibh uilig. We don't need to dream of things that never were. We have them, perhaps, are them!

Donncha O Dulaing is a much-loved broadcaster on Ireland's airwaves for a great many years, and presenter of the iconic programme 'Failte Isteach' on RTE Radio One at 10 o'clock every Saturday night.

ORIGINAL WRITING

For the past four years it has been Original Writing's great pleasure to sponsor Ireland's Own Annual Short Stories and Memories Writing Competitions. Over these years there have been many wonderful entries and it was with this in mind that we came up with the idea for this anthology.

We would like to take this opportunity to congratulate all of the winners and other authors whose writings are contained in this anthology.

ABOUT ORIGINAL WRITING

Original Writing Limited (www.originalwriting.ie) is Ireland's premier self publishing company. Founded in late 2006, we have published over 180 authors to date. While each wrote and published for different reasons, one requirement dictated the choice of Original Writing as publisher - the author, in every case, wanted ultimate control over the design, editorial and publishing process.

Original Writing is committed to publishing books affordably and to a high standard. We offer guidance to authors but unlike traditional publishers, our authors make all the key decisions about their work. Providing an array of tools and services Original Writing allows authors to make their own choices throughout the publishing process. Authors retain all the rights, maintain editorial control and choose the exact selection of services that best suits their needs and goals.

We have a great team ready to work with each author. Our mission is to ensure every author has a clear understanding of how our programme will help them achieve their publishing goals. Whether you want to get your work published for family and friends or to sell at a profit we can help you realise your dream.

We handle Autobiography, Memoirs, Poetry, Fiction - both Novel and Short Stories - Philosophical and Religious Studies, Travel Writing and many other genres.

You make all the decisions about your book with regard to content, appearance and price. We will work closely with you to turn your book into a beautifully designed and professionally printed reality. The author retains full copyright of the work throughout.

Once your book is published we will give you the tools to publish and promote your work online in front of a global audience. Your book is automatically made available for sale online and is produced on a print-on-demand basis. There is absolutely no inventory risk for the author. Copies are printed and shipped worldwide as needed.

WWW.WRITING4ALL.IE

Writing4all is an online writers' resource where you can share your creative writing - from poetry to short stories and from memoirs to novels - get feedback and comment on other writers' work. There is also news, events, competition information and listings for creative writing courses, writing groups, workshops and many more writing resources. Check out the site at: www. writing4all.ie

CONTENTS

COMPETITION WINNERS

EASTER DUTIES

By AMY MACCARTHY
St. Antonin, France

Nellie had spent most of her life devotedly looking after the parish priest without much praise or reward . . .

Nellie cut the smoked salmon in wafers and buttered them generously with cream cheese, then rolling them up, she placed them on the white porcelain plate, nudging them here and there with the tip of the knife until she formed a perfect pink rose. Her thin dry hands sped over the scrubbed deal table, which was reserved solely for the preparation of food.

She arranged Melba toast in a small silver basket and curling the butter, placed it in its dish of iced water. As she twisted the lemon slices into butterflies and placed them at the side of the salmon, she glanced at the clock and began to load the heavy silver tray, leaving the coffee pot and the small jug of thin cream, which she would bring in separately at the last moment.

Finally, like a magician, Nellie removed her coarse linen apron and whipped a crisp white lawn bib from a drawer in the table. In one quick movement she wrapped it around her spare figure, still 'girlish' in her forty eighth year and in her thirtieth year as housekeeper to the Reverend Robert McKenna, for six shillings a week and 'her keep'.

She crossed the big square hall, quickening her step to balance the heavy tray, as the grandfather clock struck seven. She heard him on the stairs, his narrow feet denying his immense bulk. Like a personal ghost, a faint aroma of lavender trailed down behind his immaculate person. White 'polished' hair, black cassock, white 'dog collar', gleaming black shoes. Black and white, the personality of the man.

"Good morning Father!"

Without looking in her direction he answered in that abstract fashion reserved for servants and people he considered inferior to himself and, sitting down, he crossed himself, spread his snowy napkin and began to eat. Finally, replete, he dabbed his lips delicately with his napkin, crossed himself again and left the dining room.

Pausing at the marble topped hall table, he picked up his four cornered tasselled hat and with the same reverence a king would his crown, settled it on his head. Nellie hurried to open the heavy oak door.

"You'll be back for lunch, Father?"

"Oh Yes! – and Father Tarrant will be here tonight for dinner at eight o'clock".

"Very good, Father – and what would you liked served?"

He was gazing across the road at the congregation beginning to trickle in to the first mass of the day.

"I think trout with almonds to start and perhaps duckling with plum sauce – I'll leave you to decide on the dessert".

He was halfway down the steps when he added "and bring a couple of the best bottles of red from below and don't forget the port!"

All this without once looking at Nellie, but never knowing it to be any other way, she smiled at his back and said "Certainly not Father!"

Accepting his rude comments and undeserved criticism when he had too much to drink and his refusal over the years to discuss any increase in the pittance he paid her, she was resigned to and, in a way, happy with her 'church mouse' existence and thanked God each night for her job and the roof over her head.

Unlike many of his colleagues, the celibacy of his vocation sat lightly on his great shoulders. Fr. McKenna didn't like women. They reminded him of distracted fowl fluttering and flapping about nothing at all. As a young boy he felt like wringing the necks of the maids who fussed about him from morning 'til night.

He was the only child of a wealthy coal merchant who married late in life an equally wealthy spinster. Children were not expected. The boy was born, like a stone suddenly tumbling from somewhere above their heads and plopping into the cold still pond of their stagnant lives. They never recovered from the shock. The house became a sea of confusion lapping about him. The parents became neurotic, watching him constantly, feeling certain he could disappear in the same traumatic way in which he had come, leaving them aimless and childless forever.

This "apple of their eye" was treated like a delicate plant. In spite of it all, Robbie grew up and out. Independent and intelligent by nature, he shrugged off the cloying attention of his timid and doting parents. He took his education seriously. His mother kept his glowing school report in her workbox. "It is clear from the above report that Robert is a student of great promise." He excelled in all subjects.

The town waited for him to blossom into medicine or maybe law. He had the appearance too, for the more sophisticated professions. Then a brilliant match would be sure to follow. They were stunned when Robbie decided on the religious life. The butcher had it first from the kitchen maid, when he delivered the Sunday joint at the weekend. He made 'great talk' of it at the counter all day Saturday.

Robert never hesitated in the long solitary journey to his ordination. His superiors at the seminary admired the good example he set his fellow students. In the fullness of time he was ordained and was sent as a curate to a small parish, half an hour's journey from the house where he was born. The bishop, a wise old owl, would not send the heir to a vast fortune too far away from it. The day of the ordination, he had clasped the old merchant's hand saying, "The boy will never be too far from you, I'll look after him and that's a promise."

The bishop knew what he was doing and so did the merchant. The next day he sent a substantial cheque to the Bishop's Palace, for use in the improvement of the local church or at his Lordship's discretion, with deepest gratitude. It was as a result of this 'transaction' that Fr. McKenna became, in a shorter time than normal, the parish priest of his home town and was able to take up residence in the elegant house where he was born, which was called Ivy Lodge, now known as The Presbytery.

Nellie scuttled down the narrow cobbled street and braced herself against the bitter east wind. She clutched the collar of her threadbare brown coat in an effort to keep out the breeze. A new coat was in order, she knew that, but every penny she could manage to save had to be put by for the day when, for reasons she preferred not to think about now, she would have to leave the presbytery. She planned to rent a small place somewhere and with her savings and old age pension, she would get by. Better suffer the cold today and be dry when the 'rainy day' came.

She turned left into a shop, over whose door the name 'Tim Bevan – Fishmonger and Poulterer' was in gold lettering. The proprietor stood there in the sawdust, in his heavy blue striped apron and rubber boots, his purple hands busy gutting a large haddock. He looked up and saw Nellie, the bearer of an order from his best customer.

"How are you Nell, girl?" he asked kindly, noticing her thin shabby appearance.

"Can't complain at all, Mr Bevan" she said, smiling timidly and nodding to his wife, a small fat woman with tightly curled hair, who controlled all from behind the narrow glass fronted cash desk at the top counter.

"And how's his eminence Nell? Minding himself as usual I suppose" he said, answering his own question, "he was ever good at that, the crafty old rogue!"

A cough from the cash desk put a stop to his flow and quickly brought him back to business. He knew the signal well. Nellie gave her order, a large duckling and two of his plumpest sea trout. He threw a lemon into her basket for luck, a sprat to catch a mackerel he thought.

"What a waste of a good woman!" he said as soon as Nellie left the shop. "It's only like yesterday she came here, poor girl, and wasted her whole life looking after that mean old crab for a few bob a week"

Nellie was back at the house at twelve o'clock, in perfect time for lunch; chicken liver pate, lightly grilled lamb chops sprinkled with rosemary, fresh garden peas, new potatoes, cheese, coffee and grapes. Afterwards, when Fr. McKenna retired to the library for the usual forty winks in his big red leather armchair, Nellie sat down in the kitchen to a boiled egg, two slices of brown bread and a large mug of strong sweet tea.

Then she furtively reached behind the big terracotta flour bin and from a packet of five 'Woodbines', she took one. Topping up her mug of tea, she settled down to her only cigarette of the day. In her mind's eye she planned the evening meal, gazing into space, relishing the taste of the tobacco and the moment to herself. Calm and contentment sat beside her.

The female population of the parish was in agreement that Fr. Jim Tarrant was 'a real film star'. Tall and fair and constantly tanned from the golf course, his even white teeth flashed on and off like a light. If the parish priest was short in the charm department, his curate was not. He had the right word at the right time for everyone, not forgetting to inquire for a sick relative or news of a job for someone out of work. He was the perfect foil for the aloof Fr. McKenna and, in spite of himself, he too fell victim to his charms.

He was amazed that so young a man should share a similar taste in music and literature and soon the curate was dining at the presbytery at least once a week.

Dinner was always followed with port served in the library and there were lengthy discussions on the latest papal encyclical or theological study. Then there were the musical evenings, when Nellie would sit on the stairs to the strains of La Bohéme or Madame Butterfly and smell the aroma of expensive cigars filtering out under the door. She was transported to all those romantic magical places she often dreamed about, those dreams being all the sweeter because she knew they would never come true.

The friendship between the parish priest and his curate did not go unnoticed by the local population. The curate, they felt, had a 'wonderful influence' on the older man. Some said he was more approachable lately. Sometimes, after a concelebrated Mass, they would talk together in the vestry and Fr. McKenna was heard on more than one occasion to laugh out loud at something the curate said to him.

They secretly looked forward to the day when a man of such a magnanimous nature would be the new parish priest. But they were prepared for a long wait, as Fr. McKenna was just fifty-eight years and never had to call the doctor in his life. He would sit it out to the end, basking in the power and the glory of his position, as all big fish do in small ponds.

Winter hung on like a chronic illness and when Easter arrived late, with its unexpected warm sunshine, spirits were lifted and prayers offered in thanksgiving in the small town.

It was a busy time for Fr. McKenna attending to the compulsory Easter confessions and other ceremonies of this festive season. It was his custom each year to entertain his solicitor, Mr Ned Duggan, to lunch on Easter Sunday. Duggan, a confirmed bachelor in his fifties, had his office in the city and lived about an hour's journey away. He was quietly charming but underneath he was observant and drew his own conclusions about those he charmed and about those who tried to charm him.

That fine Easter morning, he mounted the steps of the presbytery and raised the shining lion's head knocker, secretly smiling at the resemblance it bore to his client. He heard Nellie running down the long tiled hallway to let him in. How many Easter Sundays in the past had he heard her footsteps?

The same quick light step, never changing or slowing down since he first met her all those years ago, young, lovely and guileless, but with no social standing in the community, unlikely ever to marry or change her situation.

"Ah! Good morning Mr Duggan and a happy Easter to you!"

"And to you too, Nellie my dear" he said smiling courteously at her, putting his usual present of expensive chocolates for her and a bottle for Fr. McKenna on the hall table. He took her work-worn hand in both of his well-manicured ones and pressed it firmly.

"Its lovely to see you Nell – I hope you are not working too hard?"

"Oh, fits and starts Mr Duggan, but we must keep going, greet every day as we meet it!"

She broke off to let Fr. Tarrant in. The usual pleasantries followed when Fr. McKenna joined them and then they went into the library for a pre luncheon drink.

It was one of those rare days, calm and golden. The French windows were thrown open to the rose garden and the scent of an early lilac wafted into the room. Ned Duggan noticed how attentive the young priest was, as Fr. McKenna talked and puffed one of the cool Cuban cigars Jim Tarrant had brought him. He noticed too that he had given Nellie no little gift for all her kindness to him and the lovely meals she so often put before him. A wily young man, Ned Duggan thought, pretending to be what he isn't.

Nellie was worn to the bone after the long weekend. When the guests had left she tidied up, set up for breakfast next morning and climbed up the narrow back stairs to her room under the slates and her small iron bed with its feather 'tick'. She slept well and deeply, no coming events cast their shadows onto her dreams.

At quarter past seven, Nellie was standing to attention in the kitchen, it was unlike Fr. McKenna to be late. Still no sound upstairs and at seven thirty Nellie decided for the first time in her life to knock on his bedroom door. As she reached the top of the stairs, she heard the short sharp sound of his silver bedside alarm clock.

For some weird reason he was letting it ring. A feeling of unease crept over her and fear made her feet turn to lead. She walked slowly towards the bedroom door, bracing herself to do what she knew she must do, go in and investigate. Fr. McKenna lay 'dead as a nail' on his back in the bed where he was born. Nellie never knew how she got downstairs to call for help.

The whole town was aghast. Fr. McKenna had died from a massive coronary attack. He was buried a whole week now and though no one had seen Nellie since the funeral, when she stood at the graveside pale and wan in a borrowed black coat, everyone knew she had moved into a small room over a vacant shop in the street behind the church.

Fr. Tarrant had called Nellie to the library the evening after the burial. When she had served him a drink and he had instructed her to leave the decanter, he asked her to sit down.

"Nellie, I'm speaking to you in strict confidence, as I know you to be the most discreet person in the world."

"I understand, Father" she murmured weakly, sensing something was coming, simple as she was.

"Fr. McKenna entrusted me entirely with his personal business" the curate said, "and I have a good reason to believe that I will be taking up residence here shortly. Of course, the bishop will have to give his imprimatur, but I'm sure, when he confers with Mr. Duggan, there won't be a problem." He was saying too much, and he knew it, but the alcohol was giving him a sense of power and well being and was loosening his tongue.

"Your employment here will be ending Nellie, but I don't want you to worry. I found a very nice little room behind the church at a very reasonable rent. So have a look at it Nellie and let me know when you'd like to move in."

"Of course Father, and thank you for your help; I don't know how I'd have managed without you." Nellie knew she was beaten. She had no choice. Thirty years of her life were in this house, but they were over now. She was resigned, but heart-broken, at having to part with all that was never hers, but had over the years become familiar to her heart and to her eye.

He was speaking again – "I'd employ you myself Nellie but as you know, my Aunt who looks after me presently will move in with me. It would never do for me to leave her behind – she's a widow, as you know."

"Indeed not, Father, I understand perfectly."

So Nellie moved into the miserable little room which was to be her new home. There were a few pieces of furniture there, which she could make-do with, but the fold-up bed in the corner was in a bad state and a box supported it at one corner where the leg was missing. Dismayed at the cost of a new bed, Nellie mulled the problem over in her mind and decided to pocket her pride and ask Fr. Tarrant to give her the bed from her room in the presbytery.

"Well Nellie, I'd love to oblige you, but I haven't got the authority at the moment to move anything from the presbytery. My Aunt is getting on too and I may need it if I get a young girl in to help her. It's a big house as you know."

Nellie melted away, mortified as a whipped dog.

Ned Duggan arrived at the presbytery door with his brief case. He had been abroad on holiday and had missed the funeral, but he had sent a wire to the bishop giving him notice of his arrival.

Nellie's familiar footsteps did not hurry down the hall and he was surprised when Fr. Tarrant opened the door and ushered him into the study where the bishop sat, 'purring like a cat in a dairy', now that the day of reckoning had come at last.

Refusing anything to drink other than a large tumbler of cold water, Ned Duggan opened his brief case on the desk and carefully and slowly selected the papers relevant to his visit. When the housekeeper had still failed to appear and wishing to get on with his business, he lowered his gold rimmed half eye spectacles and looked at Jim Tarrant.

"Will you call Nellie in please, so I can proceed."

"Nellie?" Jim Tarrant said vacantly.

"Yes – Nellie – the housekeeper!" the solicitor said grandly.

"But I assumed Nellie would not be involved in this matter!" he said, amazement in his voice.

"Young man," Ned Duggan said icily, looking down his nose at the curate, "we must never assume! So, if you please, call her in here."

Fr. Tarrant was looking somewhat grey at the gills and the bishop was eyeing him like a hawk would a sparrow.

"Nellie doesn't live here anymore, Mr. Duggan."

Ned Duggan was for once in his life caught for words and beginning to fume. Jim Tarrant was losing his head and talking too much in an effort to conceal it.

"Nellie and I had a chat after the funeral and we decided she should find accommodation elsewhere as soon as possible because ...." Duggan cut him short.

9

"I'm going to have to sit here and wait until somebody gets her here and I suggest you do it Father. Tarrant – NOW."

It took another half hour before Nellie sat before the solicitor with the two clergymen and then Ned Duggan read the contents of the last will and testament of the late Fr. Robert McKenna.

After a few bequests to small charities, the main beneficiaries were named:

'To Bishop Eamonn Reid – all the monies collected from the parish and invested wisely by me over the years. (A goodly sum was named.)

'To my curate, Fr. Jim Tarrant, good friend, companion and capable assistant – all my sacred vestments and my hand illustrated Douai Bible, which I know he will always cherish.

'Lastly to my devoted housekeeper, Nellie, who came to me when she was just eighteen years old, innocent and lovelier than she ever knew, and I was twenty eight and already promised to God.

'To Nellie, who had all the trials and tribulations of a wife and none of the rewards or privileges, I leave my house and all its contents, including my beloved library and my private monies which I inherited long ago from my parents. With love, respect and everlasting gratitude.'

Nowadays, Nellie trips up and down the town in little tailored numbers trimmed with mink or Persian lamb. She has diamonds on the fingers of her slim manicured hands and has just booked a surprise Mediterranean cruise for herself and her new husband, under the name Mr. and Mrs. Ned Duggan, Ivy Lodge.

Strange to say she has only met Fr. Tarrant once in the street, when she reminded him of his wisdom in refusing to let her take her bed from the presbytery.

"After all, I'd only have had to bring it back again Father!" she laughed.

The townspeople remark on how quiet and withdrawn Fr. Tarrant has become. Of course he misses the old man dreadfully.

WHY MORETONHAMPSTEAD?

By THOMAS BELL
Killarney, Co. Kerry

*The real explanation for mother's twice yearly
excursions to visit Mrs. Powsland only came
to light after her death*

About twice a year after our evening meal, my mother would make a quiet but clearly audible announcement to me, or did I imagine it was only addressed to me? "Tomorrow we will go to Moretonhampstead to see Mrs Powsland". For all the notice my father took of this statement, it might as well have not been said – which was unusual as his was normally the dominant voice at our meal table.

For me at least, it represented some travelling and variety away from what was a fairly hum drum farming background. Mains water and electricity had not reached that farm in the 1950s, and to describe facilities there as basic would be an understatement.

Father had gone to live in at the farm aged 13 with mother joining the establishment around 20 years later as housekeeper after the death of the old farmer's wife. They decided to get married and lived there as their permanent home until the old farmer died in the late 1950s.

The morning of our trip saw me more than a little excited and also - for me – a little dressed up, clearly pleased at the prospect of missing out on a day's farm work. A bus ride took us from the farm to Kingswear station, where we boarded the train and changed at Newton Abbot for the Moretonhamstead line – the overall journey being in the region of two hours.

At our final destination, which was quite near Dartmoor, I recall walking up over a field to a cottage, where again facilities appeared minimal. Here lived Mrs Powsland, and after I had been greeted, I was despatched outside to 'have a look around and amuse myself'.

A lunch was served at an appropriate time of cold meat sandwiches and some cakes, after which we shortly departed for the return journey home. To this day I have no knowledge or recollection of what conversation passed between them on these visits. Father occasionally asked how the journey was and that was the extent of his interest.

Only after my mother was widowed and living alone, did a clearer picture emerge of what these visits could have been about. Discussing my father one day, she suddenly said ' Of course he was not my first choice you know, I was engaged to a man called Powsland and he was killed in the first World War'.

More than that she could not be cajoled into explaining, she was clearly quite choked by emotion, so it was better not to pursue the matter. Only after she died and I was going through her few effects did I get a sense of the grief and suffering she must have endured.

On the back of a magazine picture I discovered a paragraph entitled 'A Definition of Love' and I quote the first sentence. 'Love is the absolute forgetfulness of oneself in the sweet remembrance of another'.

It was easy to imagine her reading these words as a poor substitute for someone who would not be returning to a future they had obviously planned together.

The next find was a gold brooch, although subsequent investigation revealed it to be made of Fool's Gold – possibly all that a poorly paid farm labourer could have afforded in those days.

First World War evidence indicates that there were widespread sales of jewellery in this material at that time. What it does not do is diminish the thought and love that went into the giving of that brooch as a remembrance. It is engraved 'From one to another when we are apart.'

In the same album or scrapbook, were inserted a set of cards illustrating the song 'When the fields are white with daisies, then I'll return'. This was a very popular song during the War and I think they could have been given to my mother at the same time as the brooch.

The message in the song is of hope and safe return; sadly in the case of my mother and many other women it did not come true. In the album were photographs of two war memorials and I have recently made a few enquiries as to whether the name of Powsland features on either, so far unsure.

What my father thought of the situation I do not know, it could be that he knew little of the intensity involved – although I find it unlikely he would have been uncaring. He may have thought that some thoughts are better unsaid.

On my part that there are still some details to be clarified, such as where her betrothed was killed. Without doubt I will also experience some of the sadness and emotion which my mother found impossible to express.

AU SECOURS

By SANDRA MCTURK
Dalkey, Co. Dublin

Frenchie is struggling along on his own, with his dog, in the rather run-down old farmhouse until his neighbour Nell decides to take an interest ...

The thaw was as dramatic and sudden as the heavy snowfall had been. The heather and bracken glistened in the watery eye bright sunlight. As he stood looking towards the mountain, the farmer could still make out pockets of deep white. Mostly however, the brown black peat hags had reasserted themselves. It was a day to be out.

The boiling kettle called him back inside, and as he reached for some tea, he noticed that the bags of sugar filled nearly the entire shelf. He liked to make a trip into town every Friday for the fair, after which he did his shopping. Usually the same list, sausages, rashers, butter, milk, bread and marmalade. He always bought sugar and tea too, which he never managed to consume at the same rate, but habit had become compulsion and so his stock grew. He sometimes bought a hunk of salty bacon which he'd steep in a galvanized bucket until he was ready to use it.

While waiting for the tea to brew, he adjusted his leather belt by a notch. The holes were wearing wide now but he didn't feel that it would be worth his while buying a new one.

He had always been a narrow framed man, but now with buttocks shrunk within the shiny worn trousers, he looked thin. His cheeks had hollowed out too, but still retained the red veined ruddiness of an outdoor man. It was only in his own place that he went without his cap, and he had a certain naked quality without it.

He pushed the end of his shirt into his trousers as he carried the teapot over to the table. Before putting it down he had to smooth out the oilcloth, which had wrinkled under his dog's impatient paws. Next, he carried over the blackened iron frying pan which he put in a central position. This served as a plate for both dog and man. He was always glad of the extra room when the dog jumped down to find water, the rasher salty on its tongue. He liked to finish off the meal by picking out a few of the thicker pieces of marmalade from the jar, his blackened fingernails contrasting with the jewel like luminance of the orange jelly.

The wind pushed the door hard behind Nell as she stepped into the back kitchen. Her nose in a wrinkled sniff she surveyed the scene before her.

'Rough as a badgers bum, you are, and you'd want to do something about that scum-ridden bucket out the back. It's a wonder you don't get typhoid to top it all.'

Nell was a neighbour who had taken to visiting him every couple of days since he'd got the diagnosis. 'Good of her, in a way,' he thought to himself as he bit down on the marmalade rind, but he licked his fingers with more than his usual relish under her disgusted gaze.

He didn't know how she had found out his news. What he had heard about her was that she'd had a row down in the church. Always a woman of strong opinions, she didn't feel the rota of flower arrangers should be changed to accommodate newcomers to the parish. 'They'll be having bamboo on the altar next,' he believed her parting comment had been. Still, if she felt the need to make tidying up for him her latest charitable project that was all well and good. He even hoped she felt the better for doing it.

Not a man to engage in small talk, he waited until Nell had gone into the front room to set the fire before he scraped back his chair and made for the door. From a lone masonry nail he unhooked his jacket, as he was putting it on he felt her presence behind him.

'And where do you think you might be off to, Frenchie McCarthy? Didn't you hear what the doctor told you, or are you deaf and all?'

'A breath of fresh air is all I'm after.' Frenchie had not noticed before how heavy Nell had become.

'A breath of fresh air, is it? Well if breathing is such a priority with you, let you go in there and rest, the way you were told...'

She said a lot more besides as her head jerked in the direction of the front room, but Frenchie had tuned out. She was probably still talking as he gently closed the door and turned into the chilly room.

This room was still infused with his grandmother's presence, the colours of which had mellowed in the light of long years without her. Frenchie sat at the small table by the window, drumming his fingers on its polished surface. Eventually he reached under the table and pulled out a box of papers. He had always loved tracing the genealogy on his mother's side. For a while there had been an abundance of brown paper envelopes arriving at his door, their importance announced by the presence of a printed black harp.

Little paper ghosts fluttered from these envelopes. In his mind's eye, he could see his grandfather's five siblings, standing in a sloping line, like the outline of the mountainside itself. He imagined them in flimsy white cotton nightshirts, white faced with hollow dark eyes. They held hands and stared out from their premature deaths of TB at ages ten, eight, seven, five and two, four little girls and one boy, the youngest. A jigsaw of thousands, yet still half of them missing. On his fathers' side, there were no ghosts for him to grapple with, only a looming absence – a void.

'I'm off now.' Nell put her head in the door while shrugging on her coat. 'Keep that fire going, you're out of firelighters,' she shouted back as the door banged behind her. Nell had caught him once throwing paraffin from an old teapot at a slumbering fire. She had not been impressed.

Watching from the window, he waited until her blue Renault had bounced over the crest of the hill before gathering his papers together and getting up. He always worried about his flock of sheep and doctor or no doctor he was determined to look for them.

As he climbed the mountain his breath came in steady short gasps. After an hour or so he had gained a lot of height but the cold was beginning to engrain itself into his finger bones. He had no luck and was on the point of turning back when he spotted a splash of colour just north of where he was. Pausing then, he took his pipe from his pocket and lit it, sucking in the warm sweetness. He felt he might need comfort for what was ahead.

Even at this distance, he could make out the awkward angle that the body was lying at. Putting the pipe back in his pocket he moved closer. In the silence surrounding the body, he realized he was looking at a young man. He wondered how long he had lain there with only a torn bivy bag to protect him. The walker's twisted leg was obviously broken, his eyes were closed but when the farmer leant over him, he realized that he was still alive.

He considered giving him one of his two tweed jackets but then decided against it. Instead, he placed the cloth cap from his head over the man's balaclava. At this contact the walker opened his eyes, which were glazed with pain and fatigue. Grasping the farmer's sleeve he spoke urgently. The farmer released himself. Patting the man's hand he replaced it under the orange plastic and took his leave.

Retracing his steps he found that he was now walking directly into the wind. He regretted for a moment the loss of his cloth cap. The sound of the walker's urgent whispering repeated itself chant like in his head, but he could make no sense of it. Recognizing the language as French he wondered what the words meant.

As a young man he had travelled to France, hoping to find out something of his father, but the facts were too sparse. Despite the kindness of strangers he had come back knowing no more than when he had left.

He had heard people say his grandmother was a saint with all she had to put up with. They said her daughter had started off well enough, training as a nurse in Cork city, but then she had gone to England and from there she was one of the few nurses to go to France after D-Day. After the war she returned home, unmarried and with him. When he was three she had left for America, without him.

Frenchie still kept the five birthday cards his mother had sent across the ocean to him. As a child he couldn't understand it when they stopped coming despite his grandmother telling him about the accident. These cards addressed him by his proper name, Frederick; however no one but his mother had ever called him that.

To his granny he was Fred but to everyone else he was known as Frenchie, Frenchie McCarthy.

It was Pat Byrne, back with his parents from England, who had first christened him. Pat with his Liverpool accent and pile of English comics, who shouted 'French frog!' first. Finally this was shortened to Frenchie, the one word being easier to slip off the tongue for the daily taunting.

He remembered standing in the school yard head bowed while a small group would stand around him jeering, 'Frenchie, Frenchie, French frog, Frenchie.'

By the time he went to the Brothers', or big boy's school, the jeering had lessened but the name had stuck, hated at first, but then with the assimilation of repetition it had replaced, even in his own head, his mother's Frederick.

He was getting hot as he stumbled down the mountain. His breath was coming in shallow short gasps and tiredness and pain made his descent sloppy. It was inevitable that he would lose his footing, and when he did so he landed hard before taking a slide down the icy scree. The pain, sudden, sharp and exquisite, left him roaring like an angry bullock.

He was startled by a flock of black crows erupting from the beech trees which bordered the back of his land. Daylight had dimmed, and he could hear Rex, the dog, barking from the back kitchen where Nell had locked him in. He misjudged the lip of the door and staggered. The dog danced against his leg and he lost his balance kicking against the galvanized bucket as he tripped. The raw meat escaped and rolled fat side down along the concrete.

It became imperative for him to save it and pushing the dog aside he fell to his knees and grabbed it. He knelt there for a long moment clutching it dripping to his chest before slumping sideways to lie flat on the cold grey floor. Beneath the tightly held meat all he could feel was crushing pain. He thought he heard Nell, but his concentration was taken up with the tiny flecks of dust suspended in the light from the window. He watched them as they got larger and thicker and merged like a warm blanket of white snow... tucking him in... making him safe.

He heard Nell before he saw her. She bustled into the ward as if she owned it, taking in all the faces from the other beds before finding his. She knew no one in this city hospital where they'd moved him for his surgery.

'It's like United Nations in here; I thought I'd never find you. These should fit you for when they take out those tubes,' she said, dumping two pairs of yellow striped pyjamas into his bedside locker. 'They were on sale in Dunnes.'

Satisfied, she settled back into her chair, waiting to be thanked. After a few minutes she went on. 'I'm feeding the dog and John-Joe is still taking care of your cattle... if you're wondering.'

There was a pause while he didn't answer.

She continued, 'Willy found six of your sheep huddled dead in the bog. He's arranged to have them taken off the mountain.'

A memory of a face peering off the mountain came back to Frenchie. 'And what about the boy?' His voice sounded small.

She looked puzzled.

'Was there a boy found on the mountain?'

Nell had to think hard before she remembered something. 'Mountain rescue found a young fellow alright. Canadian, I think they said he was.'

Frenchie felt a sudden chill and shivered. 'Was he long dead when they found him?'

'Dead my bum, he's up in Our Lady's, his leg pinned together in I don't know how many places.' With no great interest in people she hadn't met, Nell began rummaging in her handbag. 'I got you this too, before I forget.' She slapped a plastic bottle of clear liquid on the bed between them. Frenchie wondered if it was Holy water.

'After the job they've done on you you'll need to use a hand wash. God knows what you'd pick up in these hospitals.'

It wasn't exactly the kind of alcohol that he would have wished for, but it touched him that she had thought to bring it and he found himself confiding in her. 'I saw him you know, the young fellow... the one on the mountain. I thought he was French.'

It was Nell's turn to say nothing.

'I wanted to phone for him... I wanted to help,' he said.

Nell leant over and patted his hand. 'Don't you go worrying about that lad now. Sure you know yourself. The young get over things fierce quick.'

BLESSINGS IN DISGUISE

BY PAUL McLAUGHLIN
Belfast

*Frank takes a rather jaundiced view of life from his
Belfast hospital bed, observing the goings-on around him*

❝ Boys a dear, Flynn you're the man and no messin'. Wee girls runnin' back and forth at your beck and call, three squares a day of decent grub, what more could you ask for?

"Well a bottle of stout maybe and some free baccy. Aye, now that would be a pipedream", and Flynn laughed at his wee joke and the whimsy that danced in his old medicated head and lay back in the hospital bed.

At 56 years of age, Flynn, Frankie to his old Ma, always Francis to the Christian Brothers who had beaten manners into him as an educational side effect, was now patient 1141422 of Belfast City Hospital.

He told everyone who would listen that he had been "sent to the tower block like many's the Catholic martyr" before him, but the wee girls in their B&Q uniforms, as he called them, hadn't time to listen to the bletherings of yet another middle-aged comedian. And the visitors still hadn't turned up.

Flynn lifted his morning paper and scanned the deaths' columns.

"Obedient lot these Catholics"; he mused: "They even die in alphabetical order".

Another chuckle and Flynn's paper dropped to his chest as the sedatives kicked in. Frank slept soundly through dreams of exploratory operations and benign tumours until visiting time when the hand bell clanged him awake and alone.

"How are ye love, you're certainly lookin' more like yourself."

That nice wee Missus McCarthy was peering into the bloodshot eyes of her husband, Dinny, in the next bed.

"We'll soon have you home and back on your feet, Dinny, love. Doctor says you're on the mend."

Frank closed his ears to her words of comfort.

"The lies," he thought: "The damned lies people tell to cheer up people who don't want to be cheered up. Sure Dinny's on his last legs. If that's him lookin' well, I'd hate to see him sick. I'm glad there's nobody good-mouthing me".

Frank put the headphones tightly against his ears and tuned into BBC Radio Two's history of popular music.

"Bing night tonight," he thought and nodded along to the strains of the old groaner.

"Blue Skies looking at me. Nothing but Blue Skies do I see," he mimed along with the crooner and remembered his mother singing the same song when she returned from the Gaumont Picture House.

He smiled at the dead woman's memory and the blue hat from the jumble sale that had gone to more weddings than the priest himself. He saw the fur-lined boots and the sensible skirt that saw duty seven days a week. Everything was sensible in mother's life, just had to be for mother and for him since dad had gone. The sensible shoes with their indestructible toecaps, the sensible trousers with the patch on the knee that oul Mister Jacobs next door used to call his "Admiral Nelson bags."

Sensible was a way of life in those days. No choice then. Little choice later.

Frank switched off the radio and scanned the ward. Most of the visitors had said their goodbyes and taken their boredom with them, relieved but knowing they would have to face all this again tomorrow.

"I wonder why they allow so much time for visiting," thought Frank; "When the poor oul patients can't be bothered with it and the craturs carrying the grapes and barley water would rather nip in for two minutes and be on the bus back to Coronation Street. Worse than a wake.

"Thanks be to God that nobody's coming in here to torture me," he thought for the hundredth time and rolled onto his good side to watch the kissing ritual in the adjacent bed.

Dinny raised himself onto his elbows with much puffing and wheezing while his missus placed a loud smacker on wan cheek.

"Aye, marriage is wonderful thing," said Frank to himself. "The half dead kissing the other half and always goodbye. Wouldn't it be something to kiss someone hello for a change?"

"All this lovey-dovey stuff is for the women right enough. Sure a man doesn't even think about the love thing until it's too late for the other."

He watched as the woman walked slowly from the ward, picking her steps carefully as she craned over her shoulder to take one last look back at her husband.

"God love them and be good to them," said Frank, but not nearly loud enough to be heard.

Frank spoke before Dinny had managed to ease himself back down from his awkward elbowed perch.

"She's a great girl, Mister McCarthy," he whispered: "You're a lucky man and no mistakin'. You'll have to get yourself home as quick as you can."

Dinny smiled weakly and gave Frank the thumbs up. Frank supposed that Dinny's last words on this earth would be the thumbs up. Sad but true.

Frank listened as the wheezing increased and the coughing started; great whoops of cough like baby brother Michael had had. Highs and lows coming right from his boots, Mother had said, until finally there was just a low rattle and someone went for Missus McBriarty to give the child his last wash.

Two nurses collided at McCarthy's bed just as Frank knew they would.

" Like blessed busses," he thought to himself.

The screens were dragged round and a macabre light show began behind them. Frank watched as the silhouettes did a frantic dance, hands in the air too-ing and fro-ing, whirling like

Dervishes with school teachers' voices, commanding back and forth – "Now, now Mr McCarthy get it up and it'll do ye good, get it up it'll do ye a power of good."

Frank thought of the Deer's Head pub and his first bottles of stout at the age of fourteen.

"Get them down ye, they'll do ye good," shouted the oul one's at the counter; "Best thing you ever tasted since your Ma."

He tasted again the bitter mix of hops and barley and felt the fire in his throat. He remembered the raging furnace in his head and the mad laughter, the gabblings and growlings and then the bark of the vomit in the outside toilet.

He had had to clean it with a bucket and bleached mop, clattering across the tiles as concerned customers shouted from the saloon.

"Too bloody dear to be throwin' up young lad, you'll learn that soon enough."

He'd sweated cold as the drink died in him and sworn, through the biggest tears he had ever shed, never to let it past his lips again. He had meant it. "Brother Doyle says our bodies are tabernacles that must never be defiled. God make me better and I'll keep my tabernacle locked in the future".

Of course, Brother Doyle was a half'un man as everybody knew. Sure he'd tortured the wee girls at the ceilidh on more than one occasion with the sweet desire of the whiskey on his breath and his hands where no clergyman's should ever be.

"Frankie boy, those were the days. Two bets up on a Saturday afternoon and as much stout as you could have wanted. Heaven in a public bar where the lights danced on the spirit bottles and big creamy pints didn't get time to go sour. Like a dog with a bellyful in a street full of lamp-posts. Happy days."

Frank's face turned to the present when one of the Asian doctors, "two parts coffee and one part cream" Frank called him, came running down between the beds. His shoes clicked on the tiles, a Morse message of urgency and despair.

Frank watched the shadows step up their work on poor Dinny. He was tossed and turned and lifted up and down by all three behind the screen. Encouraged and cajoled by turn –

"Come on Mister McCarthy, just a wee bit more, there's a good man, that's not so bad, you're doing great ....ach for God's sake man make an effort".

But Dinny had gone. Given up the ghost. Thumbs up to heaven and all. Frank shouted across the ward: "Let him be will ye. The cratur's had it. Let him go in peace."

Sister McVeigh reprimanded him like a nun. "No more of this carry on Mister Flynn. Down in your bed now and let our people get on with their work".

Frank knew when he was beaten. Sister was like Daddy come back from the pub with the red eyes, the black lined lips and the brassy belt buckle. "Just wait till your daddy comes home, Frankie, there'll be the belt for ye this night", his poor oul mother used to say.

Well, Frankie wasn't about to have the belt again. He turned away from the screen and put the headphones back on.

"When I'm weary and I can't sleep, I count my blessing instead of sheep and I fall asleep counting my blessings."

" I always loved oul Bing," thought Frank; "Always seemed such a nice fella, a regular guy as the Yanks used to say. The oul pipe and the golf and the wee bit of fishin'. And he was a good Catholic."

"Count your blessings Frankie and don't be wishin' your life away", mother had sung day and daily in her song of sad acceptance. Sensible and solemn and so unlike any song he had heard before or since.

He fondled his laminated Prayer to St Joseph with its promise of a happy death and whispered; "I wonder if Missus McCarthy, sensible woman that she is, will be counting her blessings tonight."

THE TWO MIRACLES

By ANDREA MOORE
Wicklow

The meeting with the 'Miracle Woman' in the sweet shop was not working out too well for the little girl on a message for her mother

Jane was one in a long line of assistants at the local grocery shop in the 50's as it was rumoured that nobody could get on with Mrs. Mulherne, the owner. The most interesting thing for me as an 8 year old was the fact that Jane had been cured at Lourdes. In a town where even the arrival of the train was noteworthy this was an event of huge significance.

I listened enthralled as the neighbours gathered together on our street to discuss the whys and wherefores of the miraculous event. They said that when she was three years old Jane had been struck down with an illness which had left her paralysed from the waist down. Wheelchair bound for the next 25 years, she had been chosen by the Lourdes Invalid Fund that year to travel to the French Shrine. The day after she arrived home she got out of her wheelchair and walked.

The news that she was now working in Mulherne's set the neighbourhood into a spin. It was as if the Virgin Mary herself had come amongst us. Like everyone else I was dying to see the "miracle woman".

I arrived home from school that Friday to find my mother waiting for me at the hall door. "Run down to the shops and get me a bottle of vinegar for the chips. Hurry now, the boys will be home any minute. There's a ha'penny for yourself". She handed me four-pence ha'penny. This was the opportunity I had been waiting for.

With pounding heart, I pushed open the door of Mulherne's shop. I was nervous about meeting Jane who for me was now on a par with the saints. The interior of the shop seemed dark after coming in out of the sunshine but soon I could make out the contents of the shelves. Tea, sugar and Fry's cocoa sat side by side with packets of Rinso, tins of Brasso and cigarettes. As my eyes adjusted to the gloom large glass jars containing Bulls Eyes, Clove Balls and Cleeves Toffees came into focus alongside display boxes of Sailors' Chew, Fizz Bags, Gob Stoppers and Liquorice Pipes.

Two bluebottles did a dance in the air before diving like kamikaze pilots onto the wooden tray of cream buns that Bolands van driver had delivered earlier that morning, while overhead large clusters of their dead relatives hung from the ceiling on flypaper. The smell of paraffin oil vied with the aromas of fresh bread and carbolic soap.

At first I couldn't see anyone behind the counter. Then suddenly a voice sliced through the silence "Wha ja want?" I looked around to see where it came from. I gawped as "Miracle Woman" suddenly materialized from underneath the counter where she had been cleaning shelves.

She was a tall well-built girl with shoulder length mousey brown hair. To call her pretty would have broadened the definition of the word. I stared at her as if she had come off Dan Dare's spaceship. When she returned my gaze I felt as if I had been beatified on the spot.

"What's the matter? Cat got your tongue?" I tried to speak but the words were trapped inside my throat. "Well are ya goin' to stand there all day?" she asked.

Suddenly, the words raced unchecked out of my mouth running into each other like carriages on a train about to be derailed. "A small bottle of Kandee Pure Malt Vinegar."

"That'll be four-pence ha'penny." She placed the bottle on the counter. Standing on tiptoe, I rested my chin on the counter where I could see her better.

"It's only four-pence in Hanleys" I said timidly, hoping to hold on to my precious ha'penny.

"Why don't you go there then" she snapped. She put the bottle back on the shelf. I didn't know what to do. If I went home without the vinegar my mother would kill me and if I ran down to Hanley's now the nun would kill me for being late back to school.

I stood at the counter too afraid to move. "Well d'ya want it or don't ya!". I nodded my head not daring to look her in the eye and handed over the money. "Miracle Woman" was proving to be a huge disappointment!

Just as I reached the door she called me back. "Hey, young wan com'ere a minute". Nervously I returned to the counter. There in front of me sat six Honey Bee Toffees in their colourful wrappers.

"They're for you but don't tell anyone" she said smiling at me for the first time since I entered the shop. I couldn't believe my eyes! It was the first time in the history of Mulhearne's shop that anyone had got anything for nothing!

That was a miracle in itself!

THE BLUE-EYED BOY

By BRIAN DONAGHY
Derry

The boys are quaking before meeting their new teacher but a lucky coincidence makes life much easier

We chatted thirteen to the dozen as we filed into the ancient desks. We were as every class has always been, 'high' at the prospect of moving in with our next teacher. He was new to our school and we'd never seen him around so Mr Molloy was an unknown quantity to us on this, our first day as his P4 pupils. We were all of eight years old.

"He slaps hard", a big P6 told somebody, "and he'll kill you if he catches you chewing gum". I there and then vowed, as long as P4 lasted, to remove penny bubbly from my eating regime.

"He'd go through you for a short cut if you have dog-ears on your homework book, my big brother says", grimaced Hughie Harkin drawing his hand across his throat. "Everybody says he crucified some boy years ago who was caught mitchin' down the country". I tried to settle myself into the allotted desk – the master had put a name on each one to ensure we sat where he wanted us to. The hard wooden seat creaked as I shifted about.

I stared at the desk top ingrained with generations of ink-filled excavations. Faceless boys had carved their drawings here and there across its worn surface. A cowboy impaled with a spear lay ghastly dead before me.

"My da says he was a killer in the army during the war and they threw him out he was that dangerous", grunted wee Jack McCallion, gravely. And Jack should have known for he may have been small but he was nobody's fool when they were scrapping in the playground.

"My da says he used to know him an' he's a hard man an' you've got to work or else . An' my da was tellin' me..." Jack was in full flow but I didn't hear all he was saying. My hands were sweating now, and I strove to find a half comfortable sitting position as my stomach began to rumble like a steamroller on the road.

A paper aeroplane crash-landed on top of the cracked inkwell in front of me as a shout went up, "He's coming down the corridor!" A blanket of silence enveloped the room and all eyes were trained on the open classroom door. Mr Molloy's massive bulk filled the door frame as he appeared, running a hand through his jungle of white hair. (This was to be his trademark characteristic, an omen we came to recognise well in the weeks to come).

"AttennnnTION!" he shouted as he entered the room, removed his gabardine and hung it on a hook behind the door. No one moved as the master glowered at each of us in turn. My right leg began to shake uncontrollably and my face felt like it was on fire.

'Duke' Reilly, seated directly behind, sniggered at my unease; and then my left leg came out in sympathy. Reilly snorted dog-like as he tried to stifle his amusement. Mr Molloy was on to him in a flash. "I'll give you something to snort and smirk about, my friend", he snapped.

Instantly, Duke became a model of decorum, sitting up the straightest in the class and wearing his most serious face. My legs continued their trembling and now my arms were joining in the activity. Try as I might I couldn't stop the shaking that had taken me over. The master reached behind the large blackboard and produced the thickest cane we'd ever seen in the school. He said nothing for a minute, then scanned the entire class, his eyes burning into mine and reading my every thought.

"This is Corporal Punishment", he announced, making a whizzing, siren sound as he swished the cane in front of him. "You'll do well to stay clear of him as time goes by." The next while he spent sorting out reading books, pencils and other textbooks and distributing them to us in class. All this was carried out with military precision and with barely a sound from any of us.

Big Danny McDermott tried to slip a brandy ball into his mouth under cover of blowing his nose but the hawk-eyed master pounced on him immediately and Danny had to throw the sweet into the fire with orders to never try that one again "... or you'll be shaking hands with the Corporal, Sir." Mr Molloy ran all his eight fingers and two thumbs through a head of thick, tousled hair as he delivered his warning.

When lunch time arrived we failed to meet the master's lining-up standards and had to sit down for five minutes, then try again to stand behind one another and walk out quietly in perfect single file. After two attempts and the loss of ten precious minutes' football time in the school playground, our performance was deemed satisfactory and the master allowed us to go outside. We knew we were in for the long haul in our new class with our new master.

All thirty-five of us survived that long first day and for the next week, miraculously, nobody's head rolled. The following Friday, after we had learnt Mr Molloy's foibles and expectations, a landmark event took place. I don't remember that morning at all but in the afternoon Mr Molloy carried out his hands-to-hair routine and we all froze.

Who was up to what? Who was in for it now? The master reached for the cane which lay on top of a pile of jotters and placed it under his armpit. He menaced towards wee Beetler Maguire who was my desk mate.

Beetler, grinning broadly, was caught red-handed holding a faded photograph as he passed it back into his school bag. Mr Molloy's large pock-marked face appeared beside us and I felt his hot breath at my neck as he apprehended Beetler. "So we have an artist in the ranks", he announced with a little smirk. "Let's view your latest exhibition." Beetler sat, his lips trembling; beads of perspiration were giving him a moustache and he shifted awkwardly in his place.

Mr Molloy pulled one hand through his hair as he grasped Beetler's photograph with the other. (The cane remained glued to the master, I noticed). He stood to the side and partly behind my desk mate. I could smell the tobacco from his clothes and counted three big blue ink stains on the lapel of his jacket as he leant over our desk.

I too, was perspiring all over; my legs, hands and face felt bathed and flushed. I could feel tears forming, hot and humiliating, as my stomach rumbled on. The master studied the photograph for what seemed an age, a wrinkled scene- of-crime exhibit, as his ample girth heaved beside me. He would eye Beetler, then the picture; his eyes narrowing while his nostrils dilated.

The tension was getting to me; why doesn't he kill us and finish with it? Beetler broke first. "It.. it's n..n.. not really youuu sir," he stammered."It..It wa..wa..was ..." I closed my eyes and waited for the cane to bisect Beetler, and then me for fraternising. A year passed and I dared to peep out of one eye up at the master towering above us.

His large chest and stomach obscured my view of his face as he removed the cane from under his arm, then placed it beside me on the desk. I could see Beetler's lips attempting to speak but he couldn't locate a single word in his mouth.

He stared straight ahead, expecting the worst. Mr Molloy uttered a kind of grunt and I dared to look up with both my eyes. His eyes had disappeared altogether, his large head fell backwards - and he laughed!

It was the loudest laugh I'd ever heard in my life! Mr Molloy was laughing! Beetler and I and the whole class for a short while were stunned; then we all began to laugh nervously, and then, as the infection spread, with more spirit. Loudest of all was Beetler as he defused his tension and dread.

The master walked back to his desk at the front of the classroom and called Beetler to follow. There they stood, man and boy chatting and smiling at one another like old buddies. We all felt lighter, relieved at this dramatic turn of events. But we were wondering, why? What was in Beetler's little old photograph that had stopped the master in the very act of murder? "AttennnTION" called Mr Molloy and we regained our composure, sat up straight and listened.

"Life's funny, boys, you know," began the master. "Years ago, when I was a wee boy, two other lads and I were fast friends. We shared our sweets, our comics and whatever toys we played with. We had many adventures together. Their names were Gerry Maguire and Oakie Gallagher – that wasn't his proper name but because he was always saying 'Okay' that was what everybody called him. We had all sorts of fun and found ourselves in scrapes too which got us into bother with our parents and teachers."

My legs had regained their normality and my stomach felt at ease again. Beetler, back in his desk, had lost his moustache, seemed perfectly at ease and wore a very proud smile.

"There are many incidents I remember from those years," continued Mr Molloy giving a mock serious scowl at Beetler "and some I'd much prefer to forget." He went on to tell us of a few boyish pranks he and his friends played on their neighbours. I was very relaxed now - for the first time since coming in to my new teacher's class - and liking Mr Molloy and his stories.

"However when I was about nine years of age my family moved to Dublin, then to London and I just lost touch with my two pals. Often I thought about them, of all our secret plans and the 'divilment' we got up to."

All thirty-five of us hung on to every word the master spoke; funny, I could clearly hear the rhythmic tick-tock of the big black-framed clock as you come in the door at the front of the classroom. I wished and prayed that the master would always be in this mood, sharing his boyhood memories like this.

The home time bell penetrated every nook and cranny of the school and, to our disappointment, Mr Molloy was forced to round off his trip down memory lane. "A little bird tells me I will soon meet my friend Gerry Maguire", motioning to Beetler, "and hopefully Oakie too after all these years". Somehow Mr Molloy's lining-up-and-filing-out regime didn't seem so regimented that Friday afternoon.

We wondered what long-ago escapade was recorded on that yellowed photograph and when we got outside Beetler divulged that he'd removed it from his dad's album after the two of them had been browsing through it during the summer holidays. Gerry senior had been relating tales from his boyhood as they'd looked at the photographs and had spoken of his bosom friend Thomas Molloy who had gone to Dublin and then to England as a young boy and who had later qualified as a teacher.

In fact he said that rumour had it that a Mr Molloy was now teaching in Derry but that he couldn't be sure and how he would love to meet up with him again. "He was a real prankster and you could always depend on him for a good laugh".

And the photograph? It showed two bedraggled, shamefaced boys, their pockets bulging with stolen apples, snapped by the owner of the local orchard as they clambered to the ground from one of his many fruit trees. There was no mistaking the young Gerry Maguire and Thomas Molloy!

The master remained strict but we felt that he was a fair teacher and grew fond of him. And for the remainder of our time in P4 Beetler Maguire was Mr Molloy's right-hand man.

THE KEENER

By JOHN HUNT
Elstree, Hertfordshire

*Young Fintan is puzzled by the peculiar goings-on between his
Uncle Jimmy and Mrs. Boyle*

I was down with measles the day we got the news Uncle Jimmy
was dead. I was seven years old and the year was 1952. There
was a terrific commotion going on outside our house as a
team of council workers, with a tar boiler and a steamroller,
laid tarmac on our dusty road for the first time. I had positioned
my bed by the pokey upstairs window to watch.

The smell of tar filled my nostrils as I jammed my head
between the cold bars and wished I could be down beside the
flames that were belching out from the boiler. There was a thin
man with curly grey hair driving the steamroller, and when he
drew level with the gable end of our thatched cottage he spotted
me, made a face and pushed out his false teeth at me. I laughed
and pulled a face back at him.

It was Mrs Boyle who brought us the news about Uncle Jimmy.
I watched her riding down the road with her dress billowing
around her sturdy legs as she peddled her bicycle. As she passed
the council workers, one of them, a red headed youth in dirty
overalls, ran along beside her and put his arm around her. "How
is the form, Molly?" he laughed. She made a slap at his face, lost
her grip on the handlebars, and fell into a trench full of nettles.
The steamroller man jumped down from his seat and heaved
her out. She wasn't hurt but her hands and legs were stung. The
driver took off his cap and whacked the youth with it.

"That fella should be locked up, Molly," he said. "Are ye all
right?"

She was not all right. She cried until she became hysterical. In between great heaving sobs her speech was incomprehensible. It was a reaction out of all proportion to her discomfort. When she eventually calmed down she made no attempt to chastise the culprit. She ignored him, blew her nose, wiped her eyes and, retrieving her bike from the ditch, wheeled it down to our gate. I was surprised to see her visiting us despite her connection with Uncle Jimmy. I thought at first she might be looking for something to put on the stings, but then I heard her breaking the news to my mother. The words, disjointed, wafted up in sombre tones from the kitchen.

"Heart attack... never know... so young... no children... fifty nine... is that all...so soon after his own woman, God rest her."

Bursting with curiosity, I ventured downstairs.

"Who's dead." I asked baldly.

Mrs Boyle turned her big wet eyes towards me, then back to my mother.

"Ought we to tell him?" My mother nodded. "It's your Uncle Jimmy Fintan. He passed away sudden...cleanin' out the taxi-" She choked. "He was taking me to town this afternoon, God rest his soul. It was his heart."

I knew what death was. I had already been to two wakes, old Johanna Dooly's and Dan Connors the tinker. I had seen the bodies and knew they would never move again. Now Uncle Jimmy was like that. They would dig a deep hole in the graveyard and put him into it. I said nothing. I just stared at Mrs Boyle for a long time before returning to my bed. She had looked uneasy when I stared at her, as though she feared I might say something.

I lay in bed reflecting on the news. I knew now that Mrs Boyle's hysterics were more to do with Uncle Jimmy than being knocked off her bike. I remembered the strange events of the previous summer when I had walked into her house unexpected.

She was known as "The Keener" around Ballyslavin. Middle aged and childless, she attended every funeral and cried copiously for whoever had departed. It was a strange affliction for someone who gossiped and laughed easily at other times.

Her husband, Martin, a large meek man who hardly ever spoke, was regarded as the shrewdest card player in the parish and was renowned for his use of the ace of hearts in the game of forty five. He would retain this wild trump and play it at the most unexpected times. His cards were always close to his faded brown jacket, his mild face expressionless, making it impossible for anyone to know what he was thinking or what he might do. When he played the ace of hearts, often at some crucial point of the game, he would push his cap back jauntily over his wispy hair, smile a pleased little smile and say: "Where did that one come out of?" Similarly in life Martin Boyle was inscrutable.

Sometimes the meaning of something you hear as a child will only crystallise later in life. I used to go to the shop for Jemmy Mooney, the publican, and very often whilst standing behind the counter, waiting for him to make out his list, I'd hear snatches of conversation I didn't understand. I remember once when Mick Dooley, the blacksmith, said something to old Sapper Cooney about Uncle Jimmy and Mrs Boyle.

"Jamsie has gone to town with Molly Boyle again."

Sapper choked on his glass of Guinness and, in between coughing and laughing, his face turned purple.

"Oh, I'd say he could go to town with Molly alright," he replied, wiping tears from his eyes.

I couldn't see what the joke was. Uncle Jimmy drove a hackney cab and drove Mrs Boyle to town every week. I, as a go between, was more aware of this than anyone. Mrs Boyle got her milk from the same farm and very often we'd meet in the lane.

"Tell your uncle Jimmy I'd like to go to town on Friday afternoon at two o' clock," she'd say. And sometimes Uncle Jimmy would reply: "When ye see Mrs Boyle tell her I'm taking the wife in on Friday to have her hair done. She can come if she wants but she might have to hang around longer than she wants."

Mrs Boyle never went on these occasions.

"Tell your uncle Jimmy I'll go on Monday, instead. I want to be in and out quick. Martin will be home from work and he'll want his supper."

It was this type of arrangement which took me into her home that previous summer. Uncle Jimmy had given me a message and I was delivering it. The house was down a lane behind the graveyard, and, from the living room window, anyone approaching could be seen. I had taken a short cut across the grave yard and gone in through the open door from the opposite side. I was very surprised to find Uncle Jimmy, in an armchair by the window, with his arms clasped around Mrs Boyle who was sitting on his lap. My six and a half year old mind didn't know what to make of it. We were all frozen to the spot for a moment, staring at each other, not knowing what to say.

"Oh, yer here," I said at last, breaking the silence.

"I decided to give her the message meself, Fintan," Uncle Jimmy managed in reply. "Mrs Boyle was puttin' up a picture there an' slipped an' fell down on me just before ye came in. Are ye all right, Molly?"

Mrs Boyle clutched her back and winced.

"It's a good job you were there to catch me Jimmy," she said.

"Don't get up until ye feel right," Uncle Jimmy advised. "Go out to the back now, Fintan and get a few logs for the fire."

I was astonished. I could see no chair, no picture, no fire, and anyway it was a hot afternoon.

"It's too hot for a fire," I said.

"It gets nippy enough in the evenings. Bring in a few logs now while yer here an' we'll set up the fire for Mrs Boyle. Off ye go now, GO ON."

When I returned with the logs Uncle Jimmy was hanging a picture over the fireplace and Mrs Boyle was clutching her back. Before I left he gave me sixpence and a sound piece of advice.

"Remember," he said, "when you're hangin' pictures to always have something solid to stand on. Mrs Boyle could have broken her back."

I was puzzled by the way they had behaved and wondered if my mother could throw any light on the matter.

"Mrs Boyle fell off a chair and landed on Uncle Jimmy," I said. "She said it was really lucky he was there to catch her. Uncle Jimmy gave me sixpence for bringing in logs for the fire."

My mother sat me down immediately and proceeded to grill me in minute detail, making no comment at all on anything I told her,

Finally, when she had gathered all the information she required, she smiled, ruffled my hair with her hand and said: "Molly Boyle has always felt the cold. You're lucky Uncle Jimmy was in such a generous mood... he's not usually very free with his money."

A few months after this incident, Uncle Jimmy lost his wife. She was a delicate woman, older than him, with a heart condition. She died suddenly in October and Molly Boyle cried at her funeral. She cried streams of tears, threw soil on the coffin, commiserated with my uncle and appeared beside herself with grief. I often saw her bicycle outside Uncle Jimmy's cottage after that, but I never went in when it was there. Some instinct told me it wouldn't be right.

More extraordinary than all of this was the death of Martin Boyle. His body was found on the 10th of March 1952 under a bridge beside the railway line, near Ballyslavin station. His bicycle was up on the road leaning against the bridge. There were fresh marks on the stone where he had climbed up. His over coat, folded neatly, was lying on the carrier with his cap on top of it. Whether he had jumped or fallen wasn't clear, but he had left home in the dark, at half past five in the morning, something he had never done before in his life.

The following day, whilst waiting for old Moonies shopping list, I heard some mysterious comments from Sapper Cooney and the blacksmith.

"Martin," Sapper said, in between long puffs on his pipe, "played the ace of hearts."

Dooley's protruding Adam's apple bobbed like a yo-yo as the drink descended his throat. He exhaled loudly, smacking his lips with satisfaction.

"Be God he did. He did, aye. He played the ace of hearts right enough. Was it anything, do you think, to do with the knave?"

Sapper chuckled. "I'd say it was more to do with the queen. I'd say she came up trumps once too often."

It was double Dutch to me. These old codgers were drunk and talking in riddles.

My mother took me to the funeral and, even though I had just turned seven, I took a particular interest in the antics of Mrs Boyle. Her grief was unbounded. She had to be restrained from jumping into the grave when the coffin was lowered. No amount of commiseration, no words, no handshakes, no embraces, could calm her hysteria. In the end Dr Brophy was called and she was sedated with an injection.

After the funeral the mourners gathered in Mooney's pub and I made a point of sidling up close to Sapper Cooney when I saw him join the blacksmith at the bar.

"That was a fine turn out, Mick," Sapper said.

"It was that," Dooley replied. "I'd settle for that meself. And didn't Molly give him a great send off?"

Sapper looked serious as he drew reflectively on his pipe. His thoughts seemed to be far away. "Aye," he said at last, "Molly Boyle is herself, an' there's no doubt about that."

I thought about all of these things as I lay in bed that morning, with the rumbling of the steamroller and the shouts of the workers ringing in my ears. I thought about Uncle Jimmy and how I'd never seen Molly Boyle's bicycle outside his house again after Martin died. I thought about how strange it was that Mrs Boyle never went to town again in his hackney cab, or how they never gave me any messages.

I was well enough to attend Uncle Jimmy's funeral which was held in Ballyslavin's graveyard on the following Thursday. Mrs Boyle was there as I'd expected she would be. Her face was white and she was dressed from head to foot in mourning black.

She stood close to the grave, still, like a statue, with the wind whipping the veil around her head. She didn't move when they put the coffin into the ground. She didn't say the responses when the priest prayed. No sound at all came from her and there were no tears on her face. She was still standing there, alone, a long time later, when I went past on my way to school.

Entrepreneurs of the 'Forties

By Gerard Morgan
Mornington, Co. Meath

*The waters of the River Boyne were ideal for soaking the Orange
'pilgrims' from across the Border*

I was reared at the bottom of Stockwell Street, Drogheda only metres from the famous or infamous River Boyne depending on your political outlook. The river played a big part in our young lives as we fished for crabs, threw stones into it, waded in it and some swam in it.

However, during the war years of the 40's it suddenly took on a new meaning. At the bottom of our street there was a big square where on Saturdays excursion buses from Northern Ireland would park and the trippers would make their way up to the town centre.

Some items during these times were scarce or maybe unavailable altogether but for our northern brethren drink was plentiful and they certainly imbibed plenty.

On their way back to their buses in the evening they would break out into song and especially the "Sash" which has a line "on the green grassy slopes of the Boyne" which told us young lads that they had a deep reverence for this river. I do not know who at first got the bright idea that we would fill up old porter bottles with the Boyne water and offer it for sale at 3 old pennies each.

We would tie a cord to the neck of the bottle and drop it into the river as we sat on the river wall and it filled with water. They lapped it up and would even drink it before boarding their buses and then buy extras and indeed some to bring home to dear old Bessie or Billy.

The business boomed and then we got wise and instead of wasting our time dipping bottles in the river we filled them from the taps in our own houses which were only 25 to 50 metres or so away and sold it as genuine 'Boyne Water'.

On a typical Saturday we would make enough money to get to the pictures for the week and to buy an abundant supply of cigarettes which we would smoke continuously in the cinema.

We even were so rich that instead of smoking our Woodbines and Players Weights we moved up the ladder and bought Sweet Afton, Gold Flake and Players to match our peers.

Well, it is an ill wind that brings no good and we were very thankful that our Ulster brethren needed their thirst to be satisfied from the sacred waters of the Boyne!

GRANDMOTHER'S PLACE

By TOMÁS HYNES
Wexford town

*Remembering many visits to a sturdy old lady
who espoused many of the virtues of the past
and liked to live life her own way*

Apassing stranger could be forgiven for thinking that there was a beehive nearby. My grandmother's drone-like and lonely chattering from behind the wartime walls of her simple cottage was within earshot from the roadway. She was as active as a worker bee. "Busy as a nailer" was her term for it.

The little garden to the front, split by a weather beaten footpath, mirrored it's keeper; colourful and full of life. It was a statement to the outside world that despite her 90 years, there was plenty of life here still. Geraniums, carnations and roses were her favourites. They came and went as nature turned. She herself was the flower for all seasons.

Her warmth and character were lavished on every caller. Stranger, neighbour, beggar and peddler all left with a story and a blessing. The only unwelcome visitor was the odd mouse who might get too fond of the carefully lain skin of a rasher; and pay dearly for it. Or a bit of damp that might appear on a wall in Winter.

She was never entirely happy with the making of that dwelling. "Thrown together with sea sand, and not fit for cattle when we arrived here in 1943", she often recalled. The roof wasn't the safest and she would even joke that it was only the moss of 60 odd years that held it together. It was very cold in Winter time and no one dared venture up into the loft. On lifting it's lid you could see the stars on a cold night.

Though her warm spirit defied all weathers, her faith was her true insulation. I made the nine mile journey from Wexford town religiously each Tuesday night. On parking under the shadow of a sycamore tree at the front gates, I made my way up the slanted cobblestone driveway through which a brave weed might have the audacity to defy her table salt remedy. I would sometimes marvel at her sitting contentedly on an old wicker chair at the Aga cooker of 1960's vintage.

A gentle tap on the kitchen window signalled my arrival and sometimes disturbed a spider nestling comfortably in a potted plant on the sill. The spider along with the robin, were her favourite creatures. She often spoke of how the spider spun a protective web over a cave to save the Holy Family from King Herod's marauding army. The robin acquired his red breast from the blood of the dying Christ as he stood loyal under the cross.

That loyalty was rewarded by the daily strategic placing of porridge oats under the tall hedge that divided her humble abode from the local national school, and well away from the reaches of crows and other scavengers. She never complained of loneliness but came to life in company. If I arrived at a minute after seven o'clock I'd be greeted by a "what kept ya?"

On entering her kitchen I joined her at the aga. The plated right hand section was usually occupied by cold feet, drying firewood or a pear softening to her liking. The simple kitchen table clothed with designs of traditional ways and days held her everyday business. Prayer books and beads, pictures, magazines, letters, a transistor radio and a fresh vase of flowers were the essential items she kept within an arms reach.

The events of the last week opened our lively conversation. Places visited, people met, housework undertaken and most importantly her future plans were all discussed. She planned like a teenager, her energy and enthusiasm defying her years.

Once everyday chat was dealt with, handpicked stories were drawn from the memory vault. My mind traversed the boundaries of time as I listened intently to stories of the character building of how a days work was done before first mass on Sunday; the pitter patter of mice running across thatched roofs as she lay snug in an overcrowded bed on real Winter nights as a child; or how the fairies created buttercups out of the gold recovered from the misers who had stolen it from the bottom of a rainbow. It was the way she told those stories that made them. She had a way of engaging any listener without doing anything other than narrating the story.

After the chapter had closed on the tales of olden times, tea and fruit cake went down as well as the stories. Often, but not until the last drop of tea was drained, she announced "Now go out to the dresser in the old kitchen. You will see a tea towel covering two bowls." Two big portions of jelly and custard would be laid out before my eyes. There was no mention of this special treat until now. I spooned the wobbling sweetness in my mouth as she cheerfully remarked "How do you like that for Irish?" It was gratitude for the company.

Our bellies full, a bird sang eight times from the novelty clock with a different species for every hour. It declared that it was time for her favourite soap, Fair City. It was the characters more so than the storylines that drew a comment or a chuckle. She took to those who shared her quick wit and humour which brought immediate favouritism for the Carrigstown mechanic, Ray.

The old bush television sat under a frosted window between the kitchen and the parlour. Granny would have the room warm already from the twin bar electric heater that rested on the grate of the now disused fireplace. Once she had covered her shoulders with an overcoat and I had placed a wool blanket over her legs, we sank into the two floral patterned armchairs that flanked the TV set.

But we never really immersed ourselves too much in the old box. Frequently, a forgotten piece of news would trickle out. Never forgotten however was another old story that sometimes broke out only to be interrupted by the phone ringing. Once dealt with, her razor sharp mind resumed her story at exactly the point she had left off, regardless of the era or length.

The 9 o' clock news and weather however, was compulsive viewing. The news reminded her of the ills of the modern world. "Power, sin, corruption and greed, that's what's wrong in the world today", she would lament. The all important weather forecast determined which day she chose for her shopping trip to town on the shuttle bus.

Goodnights all round were exchanged, from weatherman to grandmother to grandson. Promises of future visits were made before: "God send you safe son", sent me on my way to her bedroom where I plugged in the electric blanket on her bed, drew the blinds on her bedroom window and closed the door on another memorable visit.

There were times when necessity called for an unscheduled visit, such as the changing of a cylinder of gas at short notice. A large bundle of loose change would be neatly stacked on the table after many months of saving in an old jam jar. It was mostly one, two, five and ten cent coins which stood side by side like towers on the table. She knew the exact cost of the gas as well as the value of every cent counted out, just as she always had. I would then take the unbagged money to the lady who ran the village store. "Tell Bridie who sent you, she will understand, she's from my time", were my instructions.

If Winter prevented her independent feet from making the trip to town, I would be called upon to take her to Rosslare Harbour to get a loaf and a pint of milk from Murphy's to keep body and soul together. She liked to get out of the house, and was insistent on travelling with the messenger rather than have anyone bring the groceries.

We always followed the same route through Ballycogley and Killinick that she had travelled many times herself in her little car. That was before she finally succumbed to glaucoma at 89. The shopping list was in large writing, written through the lens of a magnifying glass. Her spirit did not diminish however. "God gave me perfect eyesight for so long and for that I am grateful", she said wistfully.

I always looked forward to Christmas. It was a time of double celebration as she had came into the world five days before the birth of Our Lord in the year of 1915. The name Ellen Christina reflected her timely arrival. My favourite task was the setting up of the little tree for her. The two foot tall artificial tree remained under the arch of the old chimney wall the whole year round in the old kitchen. It was once home to the aga which moved with her to the more modern kitchen built in the 1980's.

The Christmas tree lay folded slightly inwardly in a cardboard box once used for carrying the groceries. The tree was so simple and light that tightly packed old newspapers kept it sturdy and upright. I then carefully covered the box with Christmas paper depicting traditional Yuletide scenery. Then, a few small pieces of tinsel were placed under the tree on top of the newly papered box. The last task was to arrange the fairy lights evenly around the plastic branches before placing the tree on a stool in the middle of the room.

It was there that passers by could see the glow of red, green, yellow, blue and orange stars that twinkled proudly in the old kitchen. Christmas was the only time of the year that former hive of activity needed any lighting up. It was disused since my grandfather left this world in May 1981. It was now used for storage, with just enough room for feet to shuffle between the main living chambers of parlour and kitchen.

Illness eventually took her from her home of 65 years. Her last eight months were spent in a nursing home where she was never as physically comfortable. But I could sense an itch, and it was during those final few months that I came to understand what she meant by home. A place where she could see her life's work, touch her own door handle and smell the fumes of the old aga cooker. The only earthly place that brought contentment to a warm and generous soul.

The final journey she travelled with her earthly cross lasted five weeks. Visiting her during her illness was as memorable as those many trips I had paid to her down the years. Many visitors came to comfort her on her way. I sat there at her bedside through hours of deep sleep. I wondered if she was checking out heaven in advance of her arrival through those pearly gates, just to make sure her parents and nine brothers and sisters, all of whom she had outlived, were ready for their joyous reunion.

And then true to form, there were revivals for sustenance and prayer. No matter how weak she was, her lips moved in perfect synchronisation with every rosary recited in that room. And that's what saw her home. I shall never forget the final night. She beckoned me to towards her face, her glassy and tired eyes locked on mine and a little wink echoed the 'I Love You' I gently whispered in her ear. After receiving reassurances that those who were far away and could not be there were safe and well, she fell into a contented sleep and waited until everyone had left the room before finally going home to God. Just as she would have wanted, independent to the end.

Mr. Puddin'

By John Dillon

Arklow, Co. Wicklow.

*Two great friends with an interest in training and racing
greyhounds come up with a fool-proof plan to stage a betting coup
at their local track*

With a greyhound racing Stadium in the town some miles down the road from that in which the two good friends, and cousins, Dick and Mike lived, they like many others around the general area liked to keep some greyhounds to race.

Dick had a piece of land at the edge of town where they would often exercise their dogs. They would also frequently travel together to the training track and when bringing their dogs to the Stadium. They were not in the game in the professional sense but rather for the sport and enjoyment.

The lads liked to have have some kind of a bet, especially on one of their own dogs. Sometimes it would come up in conversation that they would get the chance to pull off a big win. Like one evening over a few jars Mike said "you know we have two nice young dogs so one of these nights the cards will drop just right for us and we will come home with big shillin's from the bookies". Dick nodded with a wry grin "by God you could have something in that". They chuckled at the thought of it. In those days, long before decimalisation it would not take an enormous amount at the right odds to create a tidy sum.

The chance for such a financial venture was unexpectedly on its way. One day they were notified that their two dogs were entered in the same race on the following Friday night. Mike's dog named Mr. Monday (he had bought it on a Monday) had finished second in each of the last two races of its five starts.

Dick's two months younger hound, The Phantom (thus called because he was completely coloured black) had finished third in each of his two races.

When they knew the names of the other four dogs in the race concerned they had a chat and happily concluded that they would easily have the winning of this one between the pair of them, agreeing with "we can't go wrong this time".

Having a fairly good idea of how the betting generally went on race nights they figured that Mr. Monday, having done best of the six runners would be expected to win and be a warm favourite to do so, thus leaving the prospect of good odds on the others.

However, they also knew, very importantly, that The Phantom had progressed very well recently. It had been just over a month since the two dogs had their respective races at the Stadium and in the intervening period they had brought them to the training track in another area a few times. In previous spins together up to this the younger dog had finished behind the other, but now he was flying ahead and easily finishing in front each time. The young dog was improving as he was maturing, in addition to gaining from the training experience.

Having this knowledge of what the last month's work had shown up was a gem of information for the lads. They concluded that they could pull off a pretty tidy little gamble on the race by backing The Phantom to win at nice odds. They worked it out that the only danger was within themselves which was if Mr. Monday somehow managed to reverse what happened in those recent spins.

Mike said "I reckon Mr. Monday will win races but for our purposes better not this one. So for Friday night let's take out a little bit of insurance like say I arrange for Mr, Monday to go a bit slower on the night. You know the butcher a couple of doors up from me, he makes up a lot of the stuff he sells himself". He continued '"I'll get some of his white puddin' and give Mr. Monday a bit of a feed of it just before we get to the Stadium. Tell you something Dick, them puddins are right strong whatever he puts into them. When he kills his pigs and makes up his mix

51

for his puddins I think only the grunt is left out. They won't do the ould dog any harm but will do the job for us. We are in the second race so we will be home early to have us a celebration." At that they laughed and said "let's do it."

They arranged to travel separately on the night, thinking this would be another bit of cleverality, to make it look like they were not up to anything. They met before setting out when Mike said "I put a small bit of the puddin' in front of my lad to-day and he did not seem to want to bother with the damn thing and it took a while to get him to get it down in him. I was just trying to make sure he'd eat it when we want him to".

"Ah' don't worry about that" said Dick "you know yourself what dogs are like, just wait 'till we get down the road where we intend to stop to do the business before getting to the Stadium and I'll stand my lad in front of yours and I bet your boyo will gobble up the stuff."

Later at a pre-arranged spot a few minute's drive from the Stadium they lifted the two dogs out of their vehicles and took them around onto the grass margin on the inside of Dick's car, so as not to be seen by passing eyes. Then with what they figured was the right amount of the puddin' placed on the ground, and with the black dog held just in front of him, Mr. Monday began to eat it up voraciously while eyeing the other wickedly. "Guess what" said the lads "he sure isn't on for sharin' it."

Then for a few moments while they were talking about their plan for the rest of the evening they, although well used to handling dogs, became distracted for a few moments and in an instant, quick as a flash, Mr. Monday like a rocket lunged at the other dog gripping him by the neck in a fierce bite. A right short but rough encounter took place with the two lads separating them. Soon they were driving away again, reaching the race meeting about ten minutes apart and checked in the dogs.

Then, as pre-arranged, when the betting opened on their race each of them started at opposite ends of the line of bookies and moving along placed a bet with about each third one. Thus they managed to get wagered about the amount intended at the good odds they had hoped for.

As the greyhounds were placed in the starting boxes for the race with The Phantom in number five box and Mr. Monday in number six the two pals, now that the business was completed, retired to the grandstand to watch it. Mike said "job well done I guess it's in the bag," while Dick joined in '"I'll help you count it."

When the race took off it looked like their plan was in for a big success. After a short distance their two dogs were nicely in front of the others. Soon the black dog would be motoring on and it would be collection time!

But then all of a sudden, in the blinking of an eye, their plan was turned inside out, upside down, pulled asunder and became a disaster. While the lads had forgotten all about the roadside battle at least one of the dogs had not. Running alongside each other from the start as they rounded the first bend in the race the two dogs collided with an almighty bump.

This was enough for The Phantom to remember being mauled earlier by the other. Then, despite having the racing muzzle on, he tried to grab and bite at the neck of Mr. Monday who retaliated fiercely. Very quickly, at the rate they were going, legs and bodies were entangled and the two of them became as a ball on the ground. While they were engaged in this canine version of all in wrestling the other runners flashed by and quickly the race was over with the warring dogs left behind.

The two lads in the Grandstand were shell shocked and dumbfounded by this sudden turn of events and driving back afterwards more than the dogs had their tails between their legs, feeling, as one of them remarked, 'deflated'.

When they were back sitting comfortably at home they were soon back to their normal sporting selves and figured it was a good time to take out that ould bottle of the good stuff they had being keeping in the cupboard. After a couple of drops each Dick said "sure no great harm done and we had a right craic, especially when it all happened and none of the wise guys around town knowing anything about it. I'll be smiling to myself passing some of them knowing that I have a story they'd love to get a hold of but never will."

"Same here," said Mike "and they'll never smell it."

Pouring another couple of drops Dick good humouredly said "you know some day we will have a champion hound coming along and that strong stuff our butcher friend makes gives me a great idea for a name for him and only ourselves will know how we thought of it. I think we should call that dog Mr Puddin'."

At that Mike came in with "great minds think alike." So laughing heartily, they lifted and clinked their glasses with a toast "here's to our future champion, Mr. Puddin'."

THE BEACH

By MAEVE EDWARDS

Bray, Co. Wicklow

An evocation of childhood sunny Sundays when all the family had a day out on Dollymount Strand, off Dublin's Bull Island

The two most beautiful words in the English language, according to Henry James, are "summer afternoon", and spending a summer afternoon in your favourite place must surely rate as one of life's greatest pleasures.

It is also said that when you get older you should go to places where your history is, where you know every pebble along the roadside, every tree along the way; be with people who know you and where you come from.

I am lucky, for I've never moved very far from the place where I grew up and the friends I had then are the friends I have now.

Not four miles from O'Connell Street on the Northside of Dublin lies Bull Island, with its famous wooden bridge, its pristine white sand, its dunes of marram grass, its spectacular views of Howth Head and Killiney.

It was here on this jewel of a beach that is called Dollymount Strand that I spent all of my childhood summers.

Back then on a summer Sunday, the whole of Dublin seemed to head for the coast. Convoys of Morris Minors, Vauxhall Vivas, Volkswagen Beatles, or Ford Anglias would trundle across the wooden bridge and come to a halt close to the sand dunes.

Then, all four car doors would open simultaneously and out would pour a medley of children, a mother and father, a baby in a bonnet, and a family dog.

The mother of the family would spread a rug on the side of the car facing the sun and settle herself down with the Sunday papers and a few cushions taken from the armchairs at home; the father would take up pride of place in his deck chair near the car radio on the driver's side so he could hear Micheal O'Hehir's commentary on the Sunday match. Up and down the beach, other families were setting up home in a similar fashion.

We children would change into our elasticated swimming togs, blow up our rubber rings and run at top speed for the sea. Tentative steps were taken at the edge as we guaged its coldness, but on Dollymount, the tide went out so far and took so long to come back in again that on a summer afternoon, it was nearly always warm.

Joy then when the tide was due in around 5.00 o'clock and we'd spend hours playing ball at the edge of the waves as it made its slow progress forward, teaching younger siblings to swim and digging large holes for the baby to sit in.

After an hour or two, the cry would go up from the children. "When are we having our picnic?" and eventually the primus stove would be lifted out from its cardboard box in the boot, and pumped energetically to get it going. Soon the tea would be made and we'd clear the rug of sand and set out the plastic beakers, the bottle of milk, two large parcels of sandwiches wrapped in sliced pan wrapping, hard boiled eggs, cold sausages and, for afters, a jam swiss roll.

Nothing tasted so good as that first bite into a moist, slightly soggy, tomato and onion sandwich, washed down with a beaker of warm sugary tea.

To this day, the taste of tomatoes and onions brings me right back to those sunny Sundays sitting on the red tartan rug, with my mother leaning against the car door, my father in his sandals,a knotted handkerchief on his head, my brothers and sisters so young and browned with the sun, and all of us filled with the delight of a day out on the beach.

As the sun set in the west, and we'd tired of leaping off the dunes, burying each other up to the neck in sand and had eaten up every fragment of picnic, our mother would call us for the journey home. We'd rub the sand off our bare feet and pile back into the car, grumbling that we weren't ready to go home just yet.

The baby, his cheeks flushed from the heat of the day, his small hands sticky with jam and engrained sand, would nod off on our laps as we headed home. The dog, pleasurably exhausted, would lie under our feet contented with a life that allowed him run free.

My memory always plays tricks on me nowadays as I walk along Dollymount Strand, which today proudly flies a Blue Flag. Is that my sister at the tide line digging a sandcastle just like the ones we used build, a seagull feather gracing its turrets?. And that golden brown baby splashing in the warm shallows, is he my brother?

I can hear the cries of the children leaping from the dunes as I walk and all of it warms my heart.

Highly Commended

GARDEN OF REMEMBRANCE

By GORDON WALTERS

Mulhuddart, Dublin 15

Two old World War II soldiers unexpectedly meet in Germany.

The crack of brogue shoes on cobble stone sent a tom-cat scurrying for cover. On a normal Sunday morning, the Koppel district of Cologne sleeps in a cosy silence. Only distant church bells might, now and then, disturb the tranquillity.

Patrick Hanley wasn't normally an emotional type of man yet the ornate buildings began to blur as tears gathered in his eyes. He took a deep breath and managed to force them back as he turned into a laneway. The street this led to was filled with modern office blocks. The sudden contrast of cold, stern, facades to the delicacy of the previous buildings chilled him.

"Progress strikes again," he mumbled to himself and he carried on anyway.

He crossed the road and came to a small park. Patrick stood for a moment, enjoying the scent of the freshly mown grass and then he saw that he was not alone. There was an elderly German sitting on a bench who seemed to be deep in thought. Curious, as ever, Patrick moved closer. The man seemed to be praying. His shrunken, limp, frame shivered with cold as he sat up and looked around.

Patrick had come across him before a long time ago but didn't realise it just yet. They gazed blankly for a moment, not recognising each other. Patrick moved over to another bench under a tree. The German resumed his contemplations. Patrick took a banana from his pocket and began chewing. It was a strange feeling really, sitting there in the middle of Cologne. Bananas had been an exotic luxury the last time he had been here. He couldn't help remembering how he used to lie on the grass verge of the runway, over 50 years ago, as the mighty Lancasters were bombed. Then, too, he would sip tea and eat, usually corned beef sandwiches.

As the final hours to take-off ticked away, each man's eyes would scan the horizon with ever increasing tension. The crews would amble into the briefing room around seven o'clock. Nerves began to tingle. The conversation was always clipped.

"Where to tonight?"

"Cologne."

"Bloomin' 'eck!"

"A death trap."

He didn't usually write home before a mission. On that day, though, a cold sweat was sliding down his spine and collecting in the small of his back. The flyers called it the "Death Chill". In the superstitious world of Bomber Command it spelt doom. Patrick returned to his room and, with a quivering hand, he scribbled a short letter to his parents back in Meath.

"If the worst happens," he concluded, "remember it's a sacrifice I gladly make. Freedom doesn't come cheaply."

With that, he folded the letter into an envelope which he left on his bed. The weather reports were mixed but as the moon rose it was time to take to the skies.

Patrick Hanley could never help wondering, as he nosed up into the Norfolk clouds, about the Germans he would soon be bombing. Steel-workers, bakers, widows...who were they all? What were they thinking and doing right now, all those miles away?

As it happened, one of those Germans was thinking about, of all things, romance. Gunter Goss was doing something he hadn't done in a long time. He was soaking in a bath. His mouth was dry and his heart was pounding. Tonight was the night he was to be married. The wedding had originally been intended for noon. A surprise American air raid had cancelled the ceremony which was now to take place in less than three hours time, at midnight. Gunter was already giddy with thoughts of the nuptial bed chamber, completely unaware that the Royal Air

Force had other plans for him that night. As he soaked in the water, a hundred Lancasters, pregnant with explosives, were darkening the skies over Belgium.

"This is it," thought Patrick. "Enemy air-space soon."

He steeled his nerves and put an end to his musings. From here on, all Germans, be they steel-workers, bakers, widows, or indeed brides and grooms, were no longer human beings but faceless statistics. He had to bank rapidly to avoid a colleague's plane that strayed into his flight path. It happened all the time so the incident hadn't unnerved anyone too much.

"I had a dream last night," said Arthur, his co-pilot. "We got shot down and went to Heaven."

"What was it like up there?" asked Patrick.

"God looked a bit like Hitler."

Suddenly there was shouting and panic everywhere. A Messerschmitt 109 had screamed in out of nowhere. The gunner's eyes flicked frantically around the skyline. Red streaks of tracer danced their eerie jig of death around a Lancaster below. A puff of smoke and a flash of flame. The bomber dropped into a field far below. No parachutes had been seen. After catching his breath, Patrick yelled into his intercom.

"Look out! It's coming back!"

Taffy, in the rear gun compartment, locked onto the shadow coming up rapidly from behind. The high altitude had frozen Taffy's fingers into pink icicles. He fumbled pointlessly with the trigger. The Luftwaffe fighter was on its attack path, fast and low. The Lancaster jolted as enemy bullets struck home, showering the crew with glass and steel.

"Where's the flamin' escorts?" Patrick yelled.

As soon as he had said it two Mosquitoes appeared. The German turned on his tail and disappeared into the darkness. The whole attack was over in seconds.

"Any damage?"

"Few holes here and there, Skipper. Nothing serious."

"Must be our lucky night."

Meanwhile, Gunter had slipped on his top-hat and coat and was heading for the church. It wasn't very far from his house. All you had to do was go down a cobbled street, through a short lane and there it was, Koppel Strasse Kirche.

Gunter stood in the rubble of its spire which had been snapped off in an air raid a few weeks back. All the windows had also been blown out. And so, Gunter's few guests huddled together on the same pew, a cloud of frosted breath shrouding their heads. Gunter was mesmerized when Madeleine finally appeared. She was wearing a white dress and veil which fluttered in the breeze.

And so, hand in hand, Gunter and Madeleine walked into the same chapel where they had first met when they were 13. It was also where they had stolen their first kiss, and also where they planned to have their babies baptised one day. At last it was time to put the ring on her finger.

Father Friedlich smiled. "I now pronounce you-"

The wail of air raid sirens suddenly silenced him. The congregation poured into the street. As the first bombs were released, Gunter Goss and Madeleine Emsen were finally declared husband and wife in the depths of a dank, dark bomb shelter. A quick kiss and then came their first argument.

"Forget the war," Madeleine pleaded. "Nobody knows where you are."

"It doesn't matter. You know I can't stay here. Don't worry, I'll be careful."

With that, and despite her tears, he was gone.

Most of the ordnance was falling on the western districts so, with caution, he was able to make it to the Hotel Kaiser and then to the flak gun on the roof. Gunter swapped his top hat for a helmet and sat on one of the cannons to commence firing.

The raid came in three waves. When Patrick's time came he moved into position. Even the moon had turned red in the haze of tracer, flak and blazing fires. Flak shells flew up and bombs rained down. Orders, warnings and curses cackled back and forth over the Lancaster's intercom.

Suddenly the cockpit flooded with blinding whiteness.

"Search light," yelled Taffy.

"I know! I can't dodge it!"

The light was so intense it seared into their eyes. Nobody saw the ack-ack shell exploding beneath the starboard engines. The Lancaster lurched and began to sink slowly from the sky.

"Bombs away! Anywhere. Just get rid of them."

"Roger. Bombs away, Skipper!"

"Bail out!"

Unlike in the movies, there were no stiff upper lips as the men hurled themselves out of the escape hatches.

A thousand feet below, a grim smile stretched across the face of Gunter Goss.

"Got one," he muttered to himself. But the grin faded quickly as he saw Patrick's 1,000 pounders hurtling through the sky and slamming into a nearby street. The pretty little church took a direct hit. Gunter and Madeline's special place was no more.

In the decades that had passed since, the images, sounds and smells of that fateful night had not dulled in either man's mind. Patrick had spent the remainder of the war in a Prisoner of War camp. Nowadays, all that remained of the two warriors were a pair of shrunken and shrivelled up old men sitting in a park, with only their memories for company.

Patrick finished his banana. There was a box on the bench beside the German. Patrick watched as he carried it to a bed of purple flowers. The man took something from the box, an urn. As he twisted the lid off, a tear crept from his eye and lodged in the frame of his spectacles. Feeling both moved and curious, Patrick stood up and walked over.

"You all right, mister?"

The German looked around and in perfect English whispered, "My wife."

Patrick nodded and turned to go, thinking the other man wanted to be left alone.

"She passed away on Tuesday."

"Oh," sighed Patrick. "I'm sor- "

"No," interrupted Gunter. "There's no need to say sorry. She had a happy life."

"What was her name, do you mind me asking?"

"Madeleine. Oh...I'm Gunter. Gunter Goss. And you?"

"Patrick Hanley."

They smiled, weakly. Patrick stepped back. Gunter scattered his wife's ashes over the flowers.

"She loved this little park. There used to be a church here, you know."

"What happened to it?" asked Patrick.

"A bomber," he mumbled at last. "Nineteen forty three, September the second, about one o' clock in the morning to be precise."

Patrick shifted uneasily.

"I got it with my flak gun," Gunter continued.

Patrick felt increasingly on edge. Gunter clasped the emptied urn to his chest. Patrick stumped up the courage to join him in a final prayer but the words were hollow as his mind drifted back through time. As he was parachuting from his crippled Lancaster, he was sure he saw his bombs dropping onto a church far below. His memory was a bit vague but he had thought there had been something odd about the building at the time.

"Gunter?" he asked. "Was there anything strange about it?"

"About what?"

"About the church."

Gunter shrugged.

"What about the spire?" prodded Patrick.

"It didn't have one," said Gunter indignantly. "It had been blown off a while before."

Patrick's heart dropped into his stomach. The same date, the same time, and a church without a spire.

No, it couldn't be, thought Patrick. But it seemed it was. He took a deep breath. At his age he didn't see the point in holding things back anymore. "You're not going to believe this," he began. "But I think I'm the man who bombed your church."

Gunter gazed at him for a moment. Puzzlement turned to surprise. "Are you sure?"

Patrick nodded. "I was shot down over here on the same night. Everything matches."

There was more silence.

"I know it's hard to believe. But the number of my plane was K1B. It was our tenth mission."

"But if that's the case," stuttered Gunter, "then that means I might be the one who shot you down!"

They stared blankly at each other for a moment.

"Hard to believe, isn't it?" continued Patrick.

"A bit too hard," Gunter gasped. "It can't be true."

They stood there silently, speculating on what unexplained forces of destiny had brought them together again after such a long time. They groped for some profound statement with which to mark the moment but none came. So instead they blushed with embarrassment as they fumbled through some small talk. It simply didn't seem possible.

After a few moments they walked to the gate, where they stood staring at their shoes. Patrick wanted to talk and so did Gunter. Neither quite knew how to break down the silence. Even if they did, neither knew how the other would react. So, as is the way of old soldiers, they fought back their emotions, simply shook hands, and turned and went their separate ways.

A few days later, as he was packing to leave, Patrick's telephone rang. It was Gunter. He had hunted through every hotel and guest house in Cologne and finally tracked him down. They agreed to meet in the park again, where they reflected on the war and all of its horrors.

"Madness," sighed Gunter.

"Aye. And it's still going on. They never seem to learn."

"No, they don't, do they? Bah," grunted Gunter. "If only there was something we could do to stop it all."

They both knew the modern world paid scant regard to stooped old men, so they contented themselves with swapping addresses and promising to stay in touch. The day's end eventually came, drifting in on a chilled wind. The time had come for Patrick to leave to catch his flight home.

"So long, Gunter."

"Auf Wiedersehen, Patrick."

Everything turned red, not from flame and gunfire this time but from a beautiful sunset instead. As the birds in the trees chirped and flittered from branch to branch, the two old enemies marvelled at the beauty of the world they had once almost destroyed. They embraced and the evening star began to glow in the sky above.

Time Stood Still

A *MEMORY BY* Jean Tubridy

Tramore, Co. Waterford

A daughter remembers her father's love of photography.

A week and a day after Dad dies, I find myself arriving at
Kilfarrassy beach, a few miles from Tramore. It's as if
the car drove me here, feeling my indecision.

Of course, it is an obvious place to come, over Priest's Road,
where the Strawberry Man is setting up his table with September
fruit and vegetables – a few strawberries, rhubarb, parsnips and
carrots, both with fresh clay attached.

Out along the Cliff Road, I get my first glimpse of the sea
which is at its most tranquil. Not a wave, just the reflection of
the sky, shades of blue, yellow, light grey, all in small swirls as
if on an artist's palette. It's easy to think how Dad could have
spent hours there, taking photos with his Roliflex, just waiting
for the perfect shot – the one he said would always elude him.

Instead what comes to me is his love of art. Trips to Dublin
and him and me making for the quietness of the National
Gallery, instinctively finding ourselves side by side sharing the
beauty of the paintings of the Impressionist era and our Irish
favourite, Jack B. Yeats.

What else would I give him for his 90th birthday, 15
months ago, only an art book, yet another one about the
Impressionists. We sat in the café in the hospital, he not knowing
that Mother had died only 11 days earlier, me wondering if I
would be able to hold myself together. He might have been in
a wheelchair, wearing his blue dressing gown, but through the
pages of the book, we were back in the world of Monet, Manet,
Corot, colour, health, our shared past.

Onwards to Newtown Cove; up through Lover's Glen,
where the leaves are turning to autumnal browns. Swing left
towards the solid Metal Man, standing tall over the bay. Out

past Rockett's Pub, suddenly the road with its ups and downs stretches ahead. Over the little humped back bridge near the turn off to Garrarus, gather speed to make it up the big hill towards Kilfarrassy. Thoughts of Dad reminiscing about his days with the black Morris Minor conking out on steep hills. Two big stones in the boot always at the ready to hold the car in place 'til he got it going again – no don't stop to pick up the stones – keep going to make sure to get a few more to cope with the next big hill and the inevitable stall.

Foxgloves and a blaze of Montbretia colour the ditches and, as I turn down to Kilfarrassy, I slow down to let a man riding a horse decide what's best for him. Little does he know that I'm only too aware of freak accidents involving horsemen, however skilled, talented and experienced. So often along this road, Dad has remembered the tragic death of his younger brother, Captain Michael Tubridy, world class show jumper in the late 1940s and early '50s, who was swiped from life, aged just 31, in a freak fall while schooling a horse.

Kilfarrassy opens up ahead. The car drives to the wall at the very end of the car park. This was where we sat, Dad and me, for so many hours – we were probably here this day last year.

He would look down the beach and ask if I remembered all those days we came on picnics when we were kids. And what about the day when I was three and escaped Mother's watchful eye for a second and decided to go out and swim with Dad. Oblivious to the nature of the sea, but drawn to Dad, I kept walking. Just as the water was up to my chin, Mother spotted me, screamed and Dad grabbed me and hoisted me up on his tall shoulders back to safety. Great fun for me; fright of their lives for them.

Then there was that memory of Sunday, about 20 years ago, lunch ready and no sign of Dad. Roast beef, roast potatoes, two vegetables – carrots for eye appeal and celery, because Rachel was home and it was her favourite. Mother, Rachel and I chatting away; Dad out in Kilfarrassy, up the cliffs taking photos. He said he was going, but why isn't he back? Lunch at 1.30: now nearly 3 o'clock. Sinking feelings, the clock ticking more loudly than usual, the chat turning to more than concern. Sound of car on the gravel, sighs of relief, front door opens, cameras have to be put away. Footsteps down the hall.

"Oh, you're finished." We just look at him. His radiance tells it all – no mention of worry, just listen to him enthuse about the way it had all come together: tide, waves, fluffy clouds, blue sea, golden sand and what a heavenly way to spend a morning.

"Time stood still."

NAMESAKE

By KATIE CARR

Tredington, Warwickshire

*There's a new addition to the family but a grandmother worries
that the child may be christened with an inappropriate name.*

" Isn't it great to think we're going to be grandparents?"
I said. "It's almost as exciting as having another baby
ourselves!"

"I hope it'll be a bit less work," said John.

"I wonder what they'll call him or her? I wonder if I should
just..."

"Now don't you go interfering," said John, wagging a finger
at me. "You should know better after the way my mother bullied
you."

He was quite right, of course. I'd wanted to call our daughter
Aisling, but John's mother had been appalled at the thought of it.

"If you call that child Aisling I'll never speak to you again,"
she said.

Looking back, I sometimes think I missed a golden opportunity
there, but I was trying hard to be the good daughter-in-law and
the baby was duly named Rosemary, with John's sister's name,
Margaret, tacked on for good measure.

Similar problems had arisen when my son was born three
years later.

"Whatever made you choose Alexander?" my mother-in-law
asked rather pettishly at the Christening. "It's Greek."

"So is Margaret," I said. I'd done my homework this time.

I'd never really forgotten or forgiven John's mother for putting
the pressure on me like that, though. I certainly didn't want to
be an interfering mother-in-law in my turn.

"You're right," I said now, giving John a quick hug. "Anyway,
I'm sure I'll be perfectly happy with whatever Alex and Ella
choose when the time comes."

"The time" caught up with us rapidly. It wasn't long before Ella was carrying a surprisingly neat little bump and Alex was strutting around self-importantly, holding forth on the relative benefits of investment accounts and child trusts. His rather sporty little car was replaced with a family-friendly five-door saloon with a high safety rating and the boxroom was miraculously emptied of junk and redecorated.

"It's beautiful," I said approvingly, when John and I were given the grand tour. "I love the wallpaper."

"I thought it would suit a boy or a girl," said Ella, reaching out to touch one of the little rabbits gambolling along the green gingham border. "I wouldn't want to do the 'pink or blue' thing anyway. And green is supposed to be restful, isn't it?"

"I hope so, for your sakes," said John, grinning over my shoulder at her. "I seem to remember we didn't get a wink of sleep until Alex was about eight months old!"

We made our way back down to the kitchen, Alex walking protectively in front of Ella as we negotiated the narrow stairs. Alex and his dad disappeared out to the garage to indulge in a bit of totally unnecessary tinkering under the bonnet of the five-door saloon and Ella put her feet up on a chair with a contented sigh.

"Not long, now, then," I said, sharing her sense of anticipation. "You seem well prepared."

Ella laughed. "The bag's already packed and the car gets its fuel topped up every other day. I keep telling Alex the hospital's only two miles away."

"And have you decided on a name for him or her?" I asked.

She hesitated and her gaze drifted to the tower of parenting books piled on the table between us. "I'm a bit superstitious about discussing it," she said cautiously. "It just seems like tempting fate a bit."

"Of course," I said, understanding perfectly. But when she nipped out on one of her regular trips to the bathroom, I seized the opportunity to have a quick flick through the fat paperback entitled, *Names for the New Millennium*. Several had been underlined and I quickly developed a feel for the sort of burden my unborn grandchild might have to carry through life.

"Lorenza," I read, trawling through the marked pages. "Petronelle... Virina..." The boys' names were even worse: Angelo, Deverell, Hartley. I shoved the book back into the middle of the pile as Ella tottered back and sank into her seat with a sigh.

"I was always rather glad," I said carefully, "that I gave the children simple, straightforward names. Classics, if you like – names that would have dignity and never be out of place, even if you played around with them as Rozi has."

Ella nodded. "I know what you mean," she said, "but it's nice to have something a bit different, too, don't you think? So many of my friends have called their children Rory, Joe, Bella, Katie etc."

All lovely names, I thought to myself with just a touch of misgiving. With only a few weeks left to go, I could only hope I might bring a bit of subtle influence to bear.

"Now, don't you go interfering," said John, when I was telling him about the book of baby names on the way home. "I thought we'd agreed; it's up to Alex and Ella what they choose to call the baby."

"Of course," I said, feeling a little injured by the implication. "I just want to make sure they understand how important it is to get these things right. I'd hate them to make a dreadful mistake."

A couple of weeks later, I made a trip to Alex and Ella's by myself, with an assortment of hand-knitted baby clothes my aunt had sent from Liverpool.

"I think she's had the entire Women's Institute working on your behalf," I said apologetically as I handed over the package.

"It's sweet of her," said Ella. "I'll give her a call tonight and thank her."

She looked a bit pale and drawn, I thought, but she insisted on going to put the kettle on while I sat myself down by the fire in the front room.

The same book of *Millennium Names* was on the coffee table in front of me and as I picked it up, I noticed a piece of paper tucked into the back cover. Scanning it quickly, I saw that it was a list – three names for a girl and three for a boy, numbered to give the order of choice.

"Adonia, Valida, Panthea," I read. They sounded more like the names of some of the swish cars in the magazines Alex was always drooling over. "Farrand, Radleigh, Nairn." And they reminded me of the sofas on display in our local department store. Things were not looking good for my grandchild.

I was just trying to think of a good way of bringing up the subject without "interfering", as John had so tactfully put it, when Ella appeared in the doorway. She was as white as a sheet and as I jumped up to go to her, she doubled up with a little cry.

"Get Alex," she begged, clutching the door jamb.

The ambulance arrived within minutes and Alex screeched up behind it just as they were wheeling Ella out. I stood on the doorstep, tears pouring down my cheeks; nobody had thought about locking up, of course. I phoned John and told him what had happened.

"I'll stay here," I told him. "I want to be here if they need anything."

I roamed the house, making cups of tea I couldn't drink and trying to find odd jobs to do. I wandered upstairs and peeped into the pretty nursery with its trimmed cot and matching curtains.

"Please let everything be all right," I murmured, as the tears threatened to overwhelm me again.

It was late evening when Alex phoned. He sounded absolutely drained and close to tears himself.

"Mum? It's a little girl. She's...she's on oxygen at the moment. She's early, of course, and it was a difficult birth. I'm going to sit with Ella for a while and then I'm going back to the Special Care Unit. I'll...I'll let you know how things..." He couldn't go on.

I started rambling on about other premature babies I'd heard of who went on to become strapping rugby players, but Alex didn't want to listen.

"Give Ella my love," I said, as he cut me short. I felt as helpless as he did. When I'd passed on the news to John I sat in the gathering dusk and stared at the names book, wondering why I'd ever given a moment's thought to something so unimportant.

"I don't care whether they call you Halcyon or Eglantyne," I whispered to my little granddaughter, "just as long as you're all right."

It was ridiculously early when the telephone rang the next morning, but I woke instantly, wincing as my sciatica kicked in.

"She's doing brilliantly!" Alex sounded jubilant and my heart lifted in response. "She's still in the Special Care Unit but she's off the oxygen and Ella's been able to feed her this morning. Come and meet her!"

As though I needed an invitation! I made a hasty call to John and set off for the hospital. The sun burst through the clouds as I hurried across the car park and the world was revealed in all its glorious beauty. I couldn't wait to rediscover it all with my precious grandchild.

I found Alex and Ella sitting beside a plastic tank, heads together and faces lit with pride. Ella looked tired but happy and she beckoned me forward to peer at the tiny, perfect form swathed in woolly wraps.

"She's beautiful," I breathed, watching the perfect little fingers curl and uncurl. "Just beautiful..."

"We thought we'd give her Elizabeth as a middle name, after you," said Ella.

"I'll take that as a compliment," I said, touched by the gesture. "Thank you. And what's her first name going to be? I couldn't help noticing that you'd marked some rather...interesting names in that book of yours."

Alex and Ella looked puzzled.

"I caught a glimpse of the list you'd made, too," I confessed. There was a moment's bemused silence.

"Oh, no!" Ella laughed delightedly, shaking her head. "I borrowed that book from my sister. She's been helping her local drama group write a play – some sort of a spoof of Romeo and

Juliet, I think it was. She chose some wonderfully odd names for the characters, didn't she?"

Alex grinned at me, raising his eyebrows in despair.

"Honestly, Mum, you didn't think...?"

"Of course not," I said stoutly, hoping my relief wasn't too evident. "I knew nobody in their right minds would give those sorts of names to an innocent baby. But what are you going to call her?" I held my breath.

"Grace," said Ella simply, smiling down at her daughter.

I stared at her, wondering whether she was joking. Sam patted me gently on the arm.

"It wasn't our first choice," he said. "Actually, I rather liked Amy and Ella's hot favourite was Roisín."

"So how did you arrive at Grace?" I asked slowly.

Sam glanced across at Ella and they exchanged smiles.

"Last night," said Ella softly, "when we were sitting here watching her and we were so worried..." Her voice broke and Alex took up the tale.

"The doctor came in at about midnight to check on her and he seemed surprised by how quickly she'd recovered from the birth. He said she was a real fighter. And then, when he came back the next time, he checked her over and then just looked at us and said 'Amazing!' – and straight away we both said 'Amazing Grace'-"

"And it just seemed absolutely right for her," finished Ella.

"I know you probably don't approve," said Alex. "It was Gran's name, wasn't it, and you didn't get on with her."

"Not exactly," I said, choosing my words carefully. "She could be a bit difficult at times, but her heart was in the right place. And she was a real fighter, too."

I'll admit I'd had mixed feelings, for a moment, but at the end of the day all that mattered was that little Grace was alive and well. If my mother-in-law could have been there to hear the good news, she'd have been thrilled to bits. And you never know, they might call the next one Aisling.

A Lone Goodbye

By Iain McGrath
Banstead, Surrey

Sarah is very concerned about her mother, June. June, however, has a secret that's she trying desperately to keep to herself.

" Derek, for the final time, I'm not leaving this house! Now be quiet, would you? You're giving me a headache!" June's bony fist thumped hard on the coffee table and she turned away to look out of the window.

For a few seconds, Derek just stared hard at the back of his wife's head. Their argument had been going on for about half an hour but they weren't getting anywhere. It hadn't always been like this, he reflected sadly; in 50 years of married life they had generally got on very well. But just over a year before, June had been diagnosed with leukemia and had undergone a painful course of chemotherapy, so their daughter, Sarah had suggested she sell the house and move in with her.

Derek thought it was a great idea but it was like talking to a brick wall and they had quarreled on and off for days. Why wouldn't she see reason?

"You are so bloody stubborn, woman," he said, exasperated.

June still wasn't giving an inch. "I ought to be – I had a good teacher, didn't I?"

"But you're eighty-one; can't you see this place is far too big for you? It's not easy to clean and you can hardly get up the stairs now, not with your legs."

"Oh, thanks very much."

"You know what I mean, they're only going to get worse and then what will you do?"

"Well, that'll be my problem, not yours. Now for God's sake just leave me alone!"

He was about to reply when the front door slammed, giving both of them a fright. June hastily grabbed a magazine.

"Hi...mum, it's only me," called a voice from the hallway. It was Sarah. "You got visitors? That's a nice surprise...oh!" She had breezed in, all smiles, carrying a shopping bag and looked around. Her mother was sitting in her favourite armchair, but there was no-one else in the room. Sarah blinked and put the bag down. She looked confused.

She heard me talking, June thought and quickly said, "Sarah, love, you're early. I wasn't expecting you till this evening."

"Yes, I know but I was just passing and I remembered you said you needed some milk and a few other bits so I thought...."

"Oh thanks, love, that is kind. Pop them into the kitchen, will you? I was just having a quiet read." June gestured to the magazine open on her lap. Sarah glanced at it, frowned and nodded slowly. She thought about saying something, but decided against it.

"Right, well, I'll just get these things put away then," she said absently, picking her bag up. Was she hearing things? When she'd come in her mother had definitely been talking to someone and she'd sounded upset.

As soon as she was out of the room, Derek chuckled. "It's upside down," he said.

June looked up at him. "What is?"

"Your magazine, it's upside down. When did you learn to read like that?"

She glanced down and saw with irritation that he was telling the truth. "Oh shut up, it's all right for you, isn't it?" she said in a loud whisper, "you don't have to....." She plonked the magazine back on the table.

"Nice trick if you can do it," he continued.

"You smug...you think you're so funny, don't you?"

"No, not really, mum."

June was startled and looked round. Sarah was standing in the doorway with a quizzical look on her face.

"I'm sorry, Sarah, didn't see you there."

"Who were you talking to?"

"Talking? I wasn't talking to anyone, dear."

Sarah smiled. "Yes you were, you just said 'you think you're so funny, don't you?' and when I got here just now I'm sure I heard you saying-"

"I don't know what you mean," said June. "I can't have been talking to anyone – apart from you, there's no-one else here, is there?" She met Sarah's gaze.

There was an awkward pause. I didn't imagine it, Sarah thought, she's started talking to herself but she's obviously not going to admit it.

She smiled again and looked around. "No, well not unless you've got a mystery man tucked away somewhere."

June gazed at Derek. "No," she said fondly, "no mystery man."

He smiled and blew her a kiss.

Sarah sat on the sofa. "I've put the kettle on. Fancy a cup of tea before I go?"

"Oh, are you sure you've got time, love?"

"Yes, I've got ten minutes yet." She hesitated. "Look, mum, about your phone call last night. You said you had something important to tell me."

"Yes, I have."

"What is it? Have you changed your mind about moving?"

Derek was intrigued; what important message? This was the first he'd heard of it.

June was all too aware of his presence and tried to avoid looking at him. "Well no, not exactly."

"Oh," said Sarah slightly deflated, "I hoped I'd persuaded you after our conversation last week. I do worry about you here on your own. Please, mum...please come and live with Brian and me. We've got plenty of room and we could look after you."

"Yes I know, Sarah, but I've been here for over fifty years and I wouldn't feel right living somewhere else. This is my home and I like my independence."

Sarah tried not to sound impatient. "But we've been over this, mum; when you and dad used to stay with us, you said you loved it."

Derek nodded, "You can't deny it, love, we did."

June didn't react to this and had to fight back the tears as Sarah continued. "I know you've lived in this house a long time," she said, "and it's bound to have lots of memories for you, but dad's been gone for over three years now. What's keeping you here?"

June looked straight ahead. "I can't talk about this now," she said at last, "can you come back tonight? I'll tell you everything then."

"I don't understand," said Sarah softly, "why not now? What is it, mum?"

"Sarah, don't push me, please. I can't say anything just at the moment...but I promise I will tonight."

Sarah reached over to give her mother's arm a squeeze, then stood up. "OK, mum, don't get upset. Tonight it is. I'll get your tea then I'd better be off."

A few minutes later the front door closed and she'd gone. In the meantime, Derek's eyes had never left June's face. He could tell she was struggling with something, and not for the first time he really wished he could give her a hug.

"June, what's happened?" His voice was almost a whisper.

She looked intently at him, a tear rolling down her cheek, but she couldn't reply.

"Listen," he said gently, "if I was being selfish, if I was only thinking about myself, I'd want you to stay as much as you do, but I'm not really here, you know that. If you moved it wouldn't be the end of us. This is just a house."

June shook her head. "It was our home," she said, "and it still is."

"No, love, not for three years. If you go, I'd be with you where I've been since...I... left."

"Where's that?" she asked.

"Here," he said, tapping his head with his finger. June blinked again and turned away. "And here," he added. When she looked back his hand was over his heart.

She just managed a very watery smile, "Derek Wilson...you are so...corny."

"It's true."

"I know, but there's something else."

"What?"

June thought for a moment, then reached stiffly into her pocket and brought out a crumpled letter, laying it face up on the coffee table.

"Read that," she said. "It's from the hospital."

Derek scanned the contents quickly and looked up. "When did you get this?"

"About two weeks ago."

"And you never said a word."

June dried her eyes. "No, well, I wasn't sure what I wanted to do then."

He looked back at the letter. "They don't mince their words, do they?

How long have they given you?" "I phoned them last week. Without more chemotherapy, about three months. With it, who knows?"

"Then have the treatment," he said earnestly.

June shook her head again. "I can't take any more, Derek. You said it yourself, I'm eighty-one. Look what the last lot did to me and it didn't do any good, did it? Their letter, read between the lines, 'no guarantee of success' it says. They don't want me to have it either. Look at me and tell me I'm wrong."

Derek turned away. "You've given up," he said sadly. "That's not like you."

"No, love," she said, "I haven't given up; I've just accepted it. It's my decision and you know how I like making decisions."

He nodded ruefully, "Yes, if I remember rightly you made most of mine."

She stood up awkwardly and went to sit next to him. "Derek," she said with feeling, "you say this is only a house, but it's much more than that to me because you're still here, in every room. You see, when you...when you died, it happened so quickly we never got the chance to say goodbye. I felt cheated, angry, that's why I willed you to come back. So if I have only got three months left, I want to spend them with you. I'm staying and it's no good trying to stop me."

He let out a deep sigh and for a while was lost in thought. "Sarah doesn't know, does she?"

"No, not yet, I had to tell you first. You're still my husband, you know."

He smiled at her. "And proud of it."

"I'll see Sarah tonight," June said. "I just hope she'll understand."

Derek looked anxious, "Will you tell her about...you know...?"

June laughed. "About you? If I did that, she'd have me carted off straight away. No, love, a woman's got to have some secrets."

The Bicycle Mechanic

A *MEMORY BY* Anthony Rooney
Kimmage, Dublin 12

A quick tweaking on his friend's bike almost causes a tragedy for one "mechanic".

L ike many of my generation, I left school at 14. Indeed, I left three or four months earlier. In the Ireland of the late 1940s, times were hard and jobs of any description were difficult to come by. Fortunately, through the good offices of a family friend, I was recommended to the owner of a bicycle shop in Capel Street. After a brief interview I was accepted as a messenger boy and ordered to report for work the following Monday morning.

On the appointed day and hour, nervous and excited, I presented myself at the shop, duly provided with a bicycle and told to deliver a letter to a customer in Clontarf. The bike was a 26 inch model and the saddle required adjustment by my employer to accommodate my lack of inches. I set off gingerly, but by the time I'd reached Clontarf my confidence had grown. It was a beautiful, warm day and, for the first time, I savoured the sheer bliss of cycling. The sun was shining, a soft breeze blew in my face and to my right, Dublin Bay reflected the deep blue of a summer sky.

Over the next few weeks, I was taught to do minor repairs and to add to my bliss, my employer offered to provide me with a second hand bicycle for a modest price, paid for at two shillings a week. Most of my friends had bikes at this stage and we revelled in our newfound freedom as we explored places like Howth, Portmarnock, Skerries, Bray or wherever our fancy took us.

When my friends asked me about my job I could truthfully have answered that I was a messenger boy but sadly, the sin of pride is in us all and I told them grandly that I was an apprentice bicycle mechanic. This gave me considerable status among my friends, which I enjoyed, but it had its downside; whenever a problem arose with their bicycles I was called in to repair them. Usually I could bluff my way and carry out some sort of repairs, but there was one occasion when things went badly wrong.

On a Sunday afternoon a crowd of us cycled out to the Hell fire Club; I say cycled out but in truth the ascent was so steep we walked half the distance. When we reached the Hell Fire Club, we sat and had our sandwiches, enjoyed the scenery and basked in our newfound freedom. Satisfied with our outing, we prepared for our return journey; it was then that one of the group, Malachy Foran, informed us that his brakes weren't working. As technical advisor I was called upon to carry out the necessary repairs. Full of my own importance, I turned the machine wheels up and examined the brakes. His brake blocks were worn away to almost nothing; the front brake was useless but, using a spanner, I tightened the rear one to its limits and handed the machine back to a grateful Malachy.

We began our descent and had barely travelled 100 yards when there was a shout of alarm from Malachy. Acting on the principle that self preservation is the first law of nature, we parted ranks and watched in awe as the hapless Malachy shot past us and descended the hill with the velocity of a ballistic missile. Controlling our descent by the judicious use of our brakes, we followed as fast as we could, turning each bend in terror of finding our friend embedded in a ditch or wrapped around a tree. We were almost in Tallaght Village before we came upon Malachy, standing, ashen-faced and trembling, by the side of the road. Somewhat tactlessly, I asked if he'd like me to take another look at his brakes; delicacy prevents me from repeating his answer.

In the Liberties, Malachy's descent from the Hell Fire Club became the stuff of legend; some attributed to him the distinction of being the first Irishman to break the sound barrier. My own part in the incident did not go unnoticed and I had to endure many disparaging comments on my expertise as a bicycle mechanic. In fact, two days later I was accosted by

Malachy's older brother, Tommo. Placing a shovel-like hand on my shoulder, he assured me that had his little brother suffered fatal injuries, my own demise would have followed soon after. I'm not sure if Tommo would have carried out this threat but from then on, anyone seeking my professional advice was met with an emphatic refusal.

Rogues Gallery

By Gerard O'Callaghan

Tockwith, North Yorkshire

While Mary and her mother are having tea, a shocking secret is revealed.

"You do remember," her mother said sharply, "that day we went to choose wallpaper for my bedroom?"

Her daughter frowned.

"You do," her mother said again, "I was rooting for skirts in Foleys? For the love of God, Mary, it was only a month ago!"

Her daughter blushed and shook her head.

"And I'm supposed to be the senile one!" her mother scoffed.

Mary continued to shake her head.

"Didn't we have a cup of tea with the two of them in the café by the bus station?"

The old woman was shrieking by now trying to get her daughter to remember.

Finally, Mary nodded. "I do remember," she said looking directly at her mother.

"Hallelujah!" her mother said and went to sit down.

"Wasn't that the day you insisted on having your hair done at the last minute and we missed the bus and I was late for my evening class?"

Her mother waved her hand as if swatting away a fly. "Oh, Mary, put the kettle on, I'm all upset in myself now. Poor, poor, Brenda."

As she turned to fill the kettle she heard her mother say, "Evening classes, I ask you! And he looked like butter wouldn't melt in his mouth," her mother sighed glancing out the window, pity and disappointment etched on her face.

"Do you want a biscuit with your tea?" Mary asked without turning from the sink.

The old woman continued to stare out the window.

"I'm not in the better of it. I'll have the chocolate ones, the ones you gave me yesterday were stale. I said he looked shifty," her mother continued waving a finger in the air. Her daughter laughed and banged the tea pot on the table.

"You never, you said he was very handsome and if memory serves me right, you also said that he was wearing a lovely pair of shoes!"

Her mother sat up straight in the chair. "You don't get to my age without being able to suss rogues like Finbarr Donovan pretty sharpish!"

Mary poured the tea while the old woman recalled the conversation that had taken place moments earlier in the kitchen with Brenda Sheehan.

It was just after breakfast when they heard the car pull into the yard. Mary was finishing the washing up and her mother had come in from the garden. Before either woman could comment, Brenda, ashen faced, crashed through the kitchen door, her eyes brimming with tears. She headed towards Mary with outstretched arms.

"Brenda, what in God's name has happened?" Mary wrapped her arms around the woman's plump shoulders.

"Oh, Mary, Mary," was all she could say. She turned to the older woman. "I'm sorry for barging in like this, Mrs. Kelly. Were ye having breakfast?"

"Ah no, sit down, Brenda. Mary put the kettle on and make us all a cup of tea."

Mary watched from the sink while the distraught woman pulled a tissue from her pocket. Her mother stood and patted her shoulder. Brenda and Mary had gone to school together and ended up as friends although Mary would be the first to acknowledge that the pair had very little in common. Brenda had a good job in the bank while Mary still lived at home caring for her mother. They went to the cinema a couple of times a year or met for coffee in town but that was about it. Even then Brenda always insisted her mother join them because she'd feel awful leaving her home alone.

After a few moments Brenda let out a long desolate sigh. The old woman pulled out a chair and sat opposite her.

"Where's that tea, Mary?" she barked, anxious to get to the root of the drama. "Now, Brenda, love, tell us what's happened."

Brenda turned her pale face towards her. "He's left me, Mrs. Kelly. He's upped sticks and left me."

She covered her face with her hands. Mary approached the table quietly and began sorting the cups and saucers.

"Glory be to God, he never did?" her mother said gravely.

"He did, Mrs. Kelly, told me straight to my face. He said that he's fallen in love with another woman."

"Would you like a piece of cake, Brenda? Apple brack, I made it yesterday," Mary interrupted.

"A small piece so if it's not too much trouble," Brenda replied in a fragile voice.

"Go on," said her mother loudly, annoyed at the interruption. She leaned forward.

"He said he'd met her recently and they just clicked."

"Clicked!" her mother exclaimed. "Clicked! I'll click his ears for him if I ever see him again! And where did he meet her, this woman?"

"In town," Brenda frowned as if she was struggling trying to remember.

"Do we know who she is?"

"He didn't say. All he said was it was better that he end it now rather than later."

"Try the cake, Brenda," Mary interrupted again.

Her mother turned and glared at her before turning back to Brenda. "It must have been an awful shock, pet."

Brenda nodded, closing her eyes dramatically. Finally she opened her eyes and said in a pitiful voice, "I'm just a statistic now, that's all I am!"

Mary gripped her cup with both hands to stop from shaking.

"That's men for you," her mother confirmed.

Mary banged her cup down hard on the table causing the other women to jump.

"That's a bit over the top, isn't it? I mean it's not like you were married?" Her mother attempted to speak but Mary carried on. "Didn't you say you were getting tired of him anyway, Brenda? Didn't you say to me ages ago that he wasn't really your type?"

Brenda and Mary's mother blinked as if waking from a dream.

"All I'm saying," she continued quickly, "is that it's probably for the best, especially if you were both unhappy."

"And what would you know about it?" her mother snapped. "Can't you see how upset she is? He's made a fool of her, that's what he's done. He's nothing but a cheating blackguard."

Mary stood up, her neck and face were red with anger.

"I didn't deserve this humiliation, Mrs. Kelly. Oh I've never been so betrayed in all my life," Brenda reached for a knife on the table. "He might as well have plunged this into my heart, that's how much he hurt me, Mrs. Kelly."

Over at the sink, Mary dropped her cup into sink, the crash causing the other women to stop and turn.

"What in God's name is the matter with you?" her mother shouted. "I hope that wasn't one of my good China cups."

Mary turned slowly wiping her hands on a tea towel. "Brenda," she said, trying to sound calm. "I can understand you being upset. But it was inevitable. The writing was on the wall, you said it yourself. I just think you should keep it in perspective. Perhaps Finbarr did you both a favour in the long run."

"Perspective?" her mother repeated. "I suppose you learned that at your night class."

Brenda stopped sniffling and looked up. "I didn't know you were going to a night class, Mary?"

"Art Appreciation," Mary answered flatly.

"And a pure waste of time and money that is," her mother quipped, rising slowly from her chair.

An awkward silence settled between the women. Mary was gazing outside at the withered flower pots, wishing she was somewhere else. When she turned back, Brenda was staring directly at her.

"Well, Brenda, love, it's his loss, that's all I can say," the old woman was saying in the background.

Brenda continued to stare. Mary turned away, her heart was thumping in her ears, her hands were sweating. While the old woman was offering up other condolences, Brenda went and stood next to Mary.

"When did you start the night classes then, Mary?" she whispered.

"Oh, not long."

Mary turned towards the sink and began picking up the broken pieces of pottery.

"It's just that..." said Brenda, "Finbarr started an evening class recently, I'm sure he said it was Art Appreciation. Coincidence that, isn't it?"

Mary stopped what she was doing and turned to look at her friend. All she managed to say was, "Look, Brenda-"

At that point Brenda turned and grabbed her handbag from the table. She murmured a brief goodbye to the old woman and ran out of the kitchen.

"The poor girl is beside herself," Mrs. Kelly exclaimed watching the car reversing in the yard. "Did you say something to upset her? You were very cold altogether with her, Mary. How would you like it if it was you, not that that's likely. I'll have a bit of that cake now."

Mary watched her mother walk slowly back to her chair, disappointed now that the drama was over.

She was mortified when Brenda mentioned the evening class. She knew by the look in her eyes that she put two and two together.

"Make a fresh pot, Mary, and then I might go for a lie down. I'm all upset in myself for poor Brenda."

Mary turned once more to the sink while her mother closed her eyes and sighed loudly.

She had pretended earlier that she didn't but she clearly recalled the first time she and Finbarr met in the café by the bus station. While her mother went to the toilet and Brenda queued at the counter, they had talked briefly about the weather and she had told him of her plans to attend her class that evening. She also recalled her surprise at seeing him stand outside the school later waiting for her. Afterwards they went for a drink and she laughed, remembering his passion and excitement for the subject; the serious way he looked at her when she spoke.

"You just never know, do you?" her mother exclaimed loudly from her chair interrupting her thoughts. "What a dark horse he turned out to be."

Mary sighed and wondered if she should phone him but figured she was probably too late, given the speed at which Brenda drove off down the lane.

"And she's not getting any younger, is she?" her mother went on. "It's a terrible thing to use someone like that, terrible altogether. He should be locked up, that would put a stop to his game."

Mary turned to face her mother. "He told the truth, that's all. He met someone else and he told her. She was going to finish with him anyway, she said so herself. He has nothing in common with her."

"Is the tea ready yet?" her mother replied flatly looking out the window.

"No it isn't so if you want a cup of tea you'll have to make it yourself. I'm going into town."

The old woman sat up straight and gripped the arms of the chair. "What are you going to town for?" Her mother's face took on a sudden pained expression.

"To meet someone."

"Who?"

"A friend." Mary rummaged for her car keys in her bag.

"What friend? Sure you don't have any friends, Mary. Stop now with your foolishness and make your old mother a cup of tea."

Mary was about to leave the kitchen but instead spun on her heels.

"Actually, I'm going to meet a man."

Her mother's eyebrows began creeping up her forehead.

"Actually, I'm going to meet Finbarr, mother. Yes, the mystery solved, I am the other woman!"

The old woman sat speechless. Mary found her keys and turned to go.

"We met at my Art Appreciation class."

"Well I hope you're proud of yourself." Her mother was nodding her head dramatically.

"I have nothing to be ashamed of. We get on well together so you might as well start getting used to the idea."

"I knew no good would come of this." Her mother was pointing her finger at her. "You and that bloody old night class. Art Appreciation! Nothing but trouble if you ask me."

"Oh on the contrary, it's been very enlightening. For example, I can tell right now that your face is an absolute picture!" She turned to go.

"Will you be back later?"

"Depends."

"I'll have tea ready when you get back."

"Look, I don't want to argue anymore about this, mother. I'm seeing Finbarr and that's it." Mary could feel the tears start. The terrible tension of the morning was finally coming to a head.

Her mother watched her for a few moments then stood up slowly and reached out her hand, gently touching her daughter's head. The two women stood in silence in the warm kitchen.

Finally the old woman went to the sink and filled the kettle.

"That Brenda was a bit dramatic earlier on. Did you ever see such a fuss? And we were having such a nice morning, weren't we, Mary?"

Her daughter rolled her eyes and smiled.

"Will you have a quick cup before you go?"

"Go on, then. Sorry about the cup earlier."

The old woman wasn't listening. She was staring out at the yard, her arms folded across her chest. "I admire a man with a nice taste in shoes," she said quietly to herself before turning to make the tea.

ADRIFT

BY MARY D'ARCY

Malone Road, Belfast

For Tim, a train journey away from home brings about unexpected changes.

"A great calamity is as old as the trilobites an hour after it has happened."
Oliver Wendell Holmes

D on't do it. Don't do it.
He scurried through the station, heart fluttering to the rhythm of words that had somehow got into his head, an invocation that the more he tried to shake it off, the more firmly entrenched it seemed to become.

"Excuse me." Weaving his way in and out among the commuters, he made it to the train with seconds to spare. To his relief, he secured a seat without difficulty.

He had little by way of luggage, for his stay in the city had been sweet and brief – just enough time to let them know the die had been cast and once the legal side of things was sorted, he would pull in with them. Or, more accurately, into their garage.

Tim heaved a sigh that was half relief, half regret. It wasn't the worst arrangement for a widower past his sell-by: the son and his wife on the other side of a load-bearing wall; the hospital down the road should his retina ever detach again; the church around the corner; a row of shops across the green. What more could he ask for? Yet Tim couldn't say he felt well as the train started off at a minute after ten. No.

Ever since dawn he'd lain awake on his new single bed in the new remodelled garage and stared up glumly at the new venetian blind on the new Velux window, and considered the slab of ice that had somehow lodged in the pit of his stomach and which even now, as the train was picking up speed, sent cold little shivers running through his veins and up and down his spine.

What was it, anxiety about his uncertain future? Fear of ageing? Some harking back to childhood, or even the jungle?

Don't do it, don't do it.

The rhythm of his heart became the rhythm of the train and a sudden despondency fell upon Tim. A hundred and sixty for his comfortable house, but a mere 65 for his arable land. Eighty less than Donie had hoped for. Stupid to have allowed that agent to talk him down. Why hadn't he haggled? Or drawn Walsh's attention to a fact he'd apparently overlooked: that he, Tim, had water rights, what the law referred to as "riparian". And land with water running through it.

"Okay to sit here?"

Tim looked up with a swift expectancy. A backpacker was standing there, a tall young black man who took Tim's raised eyebrows to be an affirmative, settled in and began to toy with one of those gadgets Donie and the missus carried about.

Was it iPhones they called them?

Amazing the appliances folks nowadays couldn't seem to do without, thought Tim, momentarily distracted. Things considered luxuries by people like himself and were unknown to his people before him. And not just iPhones and laptops but ways of life that boggled the mind: extensions to houses that cost as much as the houses themselves. Holidays to places only convicts ever went to. Surgery to make you look younger. Sports where you risked life and limb jumping off bridges, or diving into rapids in little rubber boats. Not that he begrudged folks, alarmed though he was for their sanity. Certainly not Donie and Anna. Their jobs demanded a certain lifestyle.

And here was something else to truly depress him: he had no idea what their work entailed. Designers of some sort, but of what?

"Websites." Donie had closed his eyes in a gesture of patient endurance. "Want me to show you again?"

No use, no use, Tim thought. The thing to do was enrol at a night school in Dublin. It might help integrate him when the pair had people over. For how often had he found himself hovering around the edges of things, heroically trying to find a point in any conversation where he could best catch hold and climb on board, as it were. And failing. Nothing for it when that occurred but to busy himself in topping up drinks, before pleading exhaustion with Anna, and slipping away to indulge his morbid talent for solitude.

It was then he yearned for Noreen, his guiding light and other half. A plain-speaking woman, she'd have piloted him through the shoals, positioning herself at the helm of conversation, steering it in interesting directions, always making sure he was on board. Poor Noreen, with that time bomb in her brain, gone behind the clanking gates of death. Without her he was adrift. No longer at home in the world.

But how selfish, thought Tim, giving way like that to despair. An insult to Donie and Anna. Had they not been kind to him, keeping in touch, arranging appointments, flying to Cork to see him at Christmas?

An ungrateful practice, surely, to imagine that beneath their kindliness he could detect a faint little thread of impatience, indifference to his lonely state and even – was it imagination - a hint of embarrassment?

"Sorry." Tim glanced up as the backpacker sneezed - a pleasant young man of about 21.

Where had he come from? Tim idly wondered. Where was he going to? Had he someone to meet him, or was he, too, wandering about in a strange land, rudderless and adrift?

Tim half-yawned and as his thoughts strayed to his little farm and his first winter away from Mallow, he heard again those fateful words.

Don't do it. Don't do it.

It was the voice of Noreen's one great friend who owned and ran The Killydoon - a picturesque pub with a quaint half-door and an open fire the whole year round. Terrible to think of her selling up, she who was the last delicate thread that bound him to Noreen.

"Have to, Timmy." Mairead had studied him with a grave reflectiveness. "But you don't have to leave here. Are you sure you know what you're doing?"

And Tim, holding his glass out for a refill, felt some sort of disturbing electrical field form around his heart. "It can be lonely above at the farm. But even if it wasn't," he pointed to the eye that had given him trouble, "the old machine is wearing down."

Mairead's eyes behind her glasses were aiming into his. He knew what those eyes saw: a man so afraid of striking out alone he would sacrifice his independence, hand himself over to people he couldn't be sure were pleased to see him, just to be safe and part of the tribe.

Don't do it, don't do it.

Mairead had clutched at the handle of the beer engine and released a swirling flood of liquid into his glass. And as he waited for his pint to settle, there drifted into his consciousness something the parish priest reeled off after he, Tim, put out feelers about moving to Dublin.

"Don't you stay at home in the evenings? Don't you love a cushioned seat in a corner by the fireside, with slippers on your feet?" Looking skywards, he'd added, "Oliver Wendell Holmes." And mulling again on those words, Tim realised with a rush of emotion that few things in life were as comforting as one's own hearth, friends and a few paternal acres.

Don't do it, don't do it. Too late, too late.

He had gone and done what they urged him not to, sold the farm the day before. And thinking of his house, its meagre contents and its only other occupant. What, Tim wondered, would he do about Laddie?

For seven years the mongrel had served him: rounding up sheep, alerting him to callers, dozing at the end of his bed, travelling with him on the tractor. Man's best friend. What were the chances the pair would allow him into their house? A vision of himself tramping the streets of Dublin with not even the dog for company rose up before his eyes, and Tim's throat tightened as he gathered his misery around him like a cloak.

"Tea or coffee?" The tinkle of a trolley one carriage up was welcome relief from his morbid thoughts. He would order tea and try to reason himself into tranquility. Donie was his only son, a 40 year old trying to make out in a fiercely competitive business in a fiercely competitive world. It was understandable he had to look and act the part. Even he, Tim, knew that success was judged through the trappings of wealth. True, it put the pair on a spending treadmill, but that was the way of the world. And he, Tim, had a duty to support the two in any way he could.

At the mention of duty, Mairead had cast her eyes up. "Yerra, Timmy, haven't you ever heard it said there is nothing more bracing for the soul than turning your back on duty?"

Tim had bridled at her tone, "Is that why you're selling your grandfather's licence?"

Mairead flamed with pardonable outrage, but pivoted round when a well-dressed man stepped into the pub and sauntered across to the counter.

"An all right time to look around?" It was the estate agent, Walsh, who gave Tim a swift acknowledging wink before raising his eyebrows at Mairead.

"An all right time to look around?"

Don't do it, don't do it.

A sigh broke from Tim as he turned his wrist and frowned at the time. Outside, the September day was bright and clear. In the distance, some golden rolls of hay scattered about a stubble field put him in mind of oatcakes slowly baking in the sun and thinking of cakes and homemade bread, and a meal he'd had at The Killydoon.

Tim sat up electrified, his brain illuminated by a sudden flash of insight. But at that moment something touched his forearm. He turned to find the backpacker leaning towards him, holding out a can of nuts.

"Like to try some, sir?"

Tim held up a restraining hand. "No, thanks, son. But tell me," He pointed to the young fellow's iPhone, "can you find information on a thing like that?"

The youth set down his can of nuts. "What did you want to know?"

Moments later, Tim, for the first time in his life, held an iPhone to his ear. He slewed his body towards the window, seeing nothing but the little pub, its white walls splashed by the yellows of nasturtiums, smoke from its chimney looping sluggishly skywards.

"Hello? It's me. I'm on the train." Tim winced at the absurdity of such an opening gambit which he'd heard expressed on train trips without number. "Tell me," His words came haltingly, "you...haven't transferred your licence yet?"

Silence. He waited for what seemed an eternity. And when Mairead croaked, "No," his heart began forcefully to pound.

"Listen, girl," Tim grabbed an anxious breath. "I know the market price for a licence. I just found out from...a young lad. And the thing is, I can afford it myself."

Thud. Thud.

"And before you ask what's going on, I'm not going back to Dublin. What I need is occupation and I'm thinking in terms of The Killydoon. We could work it together, yourself and myself. Update it, I mean."

Tim looked round, shocked to find he had an audience. And not just the backpacker who gave his best show of inspecting a map, but people across the aisle who turned away polite eyes.

He had a duty to end the call and return the phone to his benefactor. But what the hell, he thought, suddenly possessed by the demon, Rebellion. It was bracing, was it not, to sometimes turn your back on duty?

And so, he powered on. But presently, he left off speaking, for Mairead had made a sound people who didn't know her might take to be a laugh, and his expression when at length she found her voice, ran the whole proverbial gamut from hope to anxiety to alarm to relief and immediately back to hope again.

"Thanks," said Tim, some moments later as, with a bobbing Adam's Apple, he handed back the iPhone. "I've one last request before I stand ye a cup of tea. Could you write down the name o' that gadget? I've a mind to buy one for someone I know."

A Much-Loved Knight of the Road

A memory by Sean Ua Cearnaigh

Enniscorthy, Co. Wexford

To many, John O' Dea didn't look like much but he was a man with a great talent and one of the last "Knights of the Road".

During my childhood in the middle years of the last century, travelling people of no fixed abode were many, particularly in Munster. Drovers from Kerry, tinkers from Tipperary, beggar men and women from Cork, Clare, Limerick and Waterford were to be seen in all country parishes, sometimes even in the towns. Fair days in particular saw them congregate in their scores.

Fair days are now, with a few notable exceptions, matters of the past. Travelling people no longer roam the countryside, settled as they now are in houses. This is good and a sign of progress and social change. Yet, one can also lament the decline of the knights of the road. They were a colourful part of our lives and their presence enriched many communities.

Of tinsmiths, drovers, beggars and travelling chimney sweeps there were many in my native Tipperary parish beneath the shadow of the Galtee Mountains. All had their own traits and habits. Perhaps the best loved of them all was a native of East Limerick. John O'Dea, invariably known as "Jack Day", had been a drover in his early years. By the time he appeared in our parish he was middle-aged and had long abandoned his early trade. He was a small genial man who always wore a weather-beaten hat. He had an excellent repertoire of popular Irish ballads, which he sang in licensed premises and in houses where he was given lodgings for the night. Jack was not fond of work, nor did the families who put him up for the night expect him to help them in their daily chores. His singing was ample recompense. He had fine songs: "Kevin Barry", "The Rose of Mooncoin", "Galway Bay" and many more. His favourite song was a homely ballad, presumably from his native county called, "The Grand Old Lady Murphy O'". Who the grand old lady was we never knew, but she was obviously no aristocrat. Jack was illiterate and had all his songs from memory. Once my youngest sister took down from him the words of "The Grand Old Lady Murphy O'". Jack could not recall certain lines offhand, particularly those in the middle of verses. So when my sister, Ann wrote down the song, Jack had to sing whole verses over and over again in order that individual lines could be captured.

Once he called at night while our parents were out. We entertained him as usual and made tea for him while he, in turn, took a packet of bulls eyes from his pocket which he distributed amongst us. We enjoyed them greatly.

He often called to our thatched farmhouse and was always warmly welcomed. My father, in particular, himself a man of music, loved to see him. Jack recalled many memories of his past. One memory, which was not so pleasant, was his totally undeserved short term in prison. He had once imbibed a little too freely in a certain Cork town. An over zealous garda arrested him. Charged with drunkenness and vagrancy, he was sentenced to a week in prison. Jack, a saintly and upright man, was mortified. To the end of his days he never returned to the town where he had been arrested. He was, as already noted, a saintly man.

When in our house, he slept on the mattress laid out for him in the kitchen. We could hear him saying the Rosary and many other prayers in his slow sing-song voice. We, as disrespectful youngsters, listened and laughed our heads off. Poor Jack! Did he hear us and if so, what did he think of us?

Jack sometimes visited the local licensed premises. Here he sang his ballads for the entertainment of the local clientele and was duly rewarded when drinkers, in calling their rounds, included him also. Such evenings cheered him up greatly. Sometimes he slept on an improvised bed in the licensed premises but more usually as a guest of some patron of the pub. Our little South Tipperary community always accorded him a hearty "céad mile fáilte", which he greatly appreciated. As the years passed by, Jack, now old and no doubt feeling the need for company, acquired dogs. He now had a dog accompanying him always and, as each dog died, he replaced him with another, usually a present of an unwanted animal from somebody or other. On one occasion (and one could see that some trickster had a hand in this), he told us that there were papers going with his dog. A pedigree animal, no less! When we asked him to show us these papers it turned out to be a disused radio licence. Jack couldn't read, something the presenter of the licence knew very well. No more honest or upright person roamed the roads of Tipperary. He once found a wallet containing over £100 on the road near the village of Ballylooby. He immediately handed it in at the local Garda station and the sergeant promised that he would institute enquiries and, perhaps, locate the owner. In due course he discovered the owner who had mislaid the wallet. The person in question, a tight-fisted man, thanked the sergeant but said nothing of rewarding the finder. The sergeant promptly asked him to hand back the wallet which he did with some reluctance. The sergeant then extracted a £10 note.

"This," he said to the tight-fisted man as he handed him back his wallet, "goes to Jack Day."

When Jack next visited Ballylooby, the sergeant handed him his reward. Jack was overjoyed, having never had so much money before.

Jack was about 70 years old when he died, by strange coincidence on the same day as his fellow county man, Éamonn de Valera. Following his death, generous tributes to him were penned in the Clonmel paper, *The Nationalist* and also in, *The Limerick Leader*. It is not often that a man receives written obituarial accolades in two counties but John O'Dea/Jack Day surely deserved them. Beannacht dílis Dé lena anam uasal.

Love Knows No Bounds

By Elizabeth Brennan
Castlecomer, Co. Kilkenny

A new arrival to the village prompts much interest from the locals.

She arrived on a bright June morning on Toohey's bus. It was Jane Hegarty who saw her first as she got off at the post office and with a little help from the bus driver, pulled the large tattered suitcase from the boot. It was tied with large leather straps and was bulging at all four corners. When she had settled herself, thrown back the voluminous orange, cotton shawl over her shoulders and smoothed down her thick auburn hair, she crossed the street with a jaunty skip and enquired the way to Tom Mack's cottage. Jane was stunned, especially as she detected the slight hint of a foreign accent in her voice. The cottage had lain idle for more than a year since Tom's mother died, although she did remember he had painted it and trimmed the hedges and flowerbeds early in the spring.

"You're almost there, love," Jane spluttered. "Take the first right below the turn and you can't miss it. It's the cottage with the bright red door on the left."

"You are very kind," she answered with a smile, took up her weighty case and set off.

Jane Hegarty lost no time in informing the whole village of the new arrival. Everyone was puzzled as to how somebody from abroad had discovered their village, tucked away under Slieve an Iarainn - a stone's throw from the Atlantic Ocean. It was off the beaten track and had little to recommend it except the roar of the sea and the constant screech of the seagulls. Everyone was curious as to how she was going to earn a living and support herself. Work wasn't plentiful in the area and most of the locals had to travel by car to Westport or Claremorris for employment. Tom Mack, of course, was tight lipped and refused to reveal any details. All he would say was he thought that she came from somewhere on the continent. He could make "no offer" he said at pronouncing her name.

All that summer she set Gortaguileen on fire. Villagers stood in awe as she skipped down the bohereens, her hair flying in the breeze and her large brown sack bag under her arm. By now it was evident that she was an artist. She had been spotted several times by the shore with her easel and brushes. As summer turned to autumn and autumn to winter, the carefree summer dress of the stranger changed to more comfortable attire: thick coloured stockings of purple, orange and red and sensible boots. In time she became known to the whole village as "Stockings". The women envied her and were more than a little jealous as their men folk could talk of nothing else. Few dared approach her other than to reply to her cheery greeting as they met her on her walks, with her skirts and shawls floating in the breeze.

As the harvest time dance approached, the village was agog with expectation. Would she come? Should someone invite her? As it turned out, no one could find the courage to approach her or an excuse to ask her. They needn't have worried. It was in the middle of the Siege of Ennis that the door of the hall opened. All eyes turned. There she stood, her auburn hair in long curls over her shoulders and her bright red stockings visible under her long black skirt, her face beaming with a smile as her eyes moved from side to side taking in the scene. She seemed to stand there for an eternity. Everybody looked from one to the other not sure what to do. It was then that "Be Nice" got up from his seat at the back of the hall and headed for the door. "Be Nice" or John Tolan to give him his proper name, had earned his nickname from his habit of continually pronouncing, "it costs nothing to be nice." John, in his early 40s had never married. No one could remember if he ever had a girlfriend and while his mother was alive there was no question of bringing home a girl. He strode over to her and after a few words, whispered in her ear. She followed him, all smiles, back to the end of the hall and sat on the vacant seat next to him.

Typical of Be Nice, thought Jane Hegarty as she set out the cups and saucers for the supper.

It wasn't long before they were in deep conversation. Be Nice was never one to engage in long conversation, but this was different. He talked and laughed with Stockings and seemed never to be stuck for words. They sat out the next few dances together until supper was called. As the music stopped, Be Nice bounded up to the long table at the other end of the hall and filled two plates with buns and sandwiches and returned for two cups of tea. Nobody could concentrate on the supper as everybody tried to catch a sneaky glance at the pair.

As supper finished, the slow waltz was called and the music started again. Judy Murray and Mick Lyng always led the waltzers and as the floor filled up a little, Be Nice led the reluctant Stockings carefully on to the floor. They counted and chased and it wasn't long before Stockings was moving with ease and following Be Nice's well directed steps. It didn't escape the notice of the other dancers the way he pulled her to himself on the corners or laid his right arm across her back between the dances. No one had ever seen Be Nice smile so much.

In the weeks that followed they could be seen walking the shore together, heads thrown back in laughter or on Be Nice's old Massey Ferguson as he took hay to cattle up on the Mointeach. As the days lengthened in April and early May, they cycled and collected spring flowers, fished in the stream or sat for hours as she painted by the shore. Nothing escaped the prying eyes and ears of the curious neighbours.

Be Nice was setting himself up for heartbreak, they thought. But as summer wore on and Be Nice engaged the local carpenter and plumber to install a new kitchen and bathroom and ordered a new double bed from the furniture shop in Westport, reality dawned on them. There was a wedding in the air.

Jane Hegarty was beside herself with excitement. "The cutest of hens lay out," was all she could say. And so it was that Marie-Angelique Lemonier from St. Guilhem in France and John Patrick Tolan were married in the parish church of Gortaguileen on a sunny September day. John walked up the aisle in his white linen open necked shirt and his bride carried a bouquet of wild fuchsia with a wreath of daisies in her hair, where they were pronounced man and wife. By then the whole village was on first name terms with Marie-Ange, laughing and joking with her, the nickname gone forever.

In time, she and John would rear a family of four children and as they grew up, he constantly impressed on them, "it costs nothing to be nice." On quiet summer evenings as you passed the cottage and above the din of playing children, you would hear John call, "Angelique, ma belle, ma puce, je suis là" as he came in from the yard after a long day on the bog or in the meadow. She would answer the call and in seconds he would lift her off the ground, hold her closely and swing her around to her screams of "laisse moi, laisse moi." Then planting a kiss on her upturned mouth, they would walk hand in hand to the door.

The Last Right

By PAULINE BURGESS

Carryduff, Belfast

*Mary begins her search to find something so dear to her that she
lost long ago.*

Mary Hogan had been beautiful once, but now she's like a painting that has been left out in the sun too long: faded and obscured. She has worn her silence like a piece of skin for so many years that it's impossible to see beyond it. Just over a week ago her doctor told her to put her things in order, and now here she is ensconced in the musty waiting room of Johnson and Johnson, sipping on weak tea and wishing she was at home.

"Mrs. Hogan? Mr. Johnson apologises for the delay. He says someone will be with you shortly."

Mary smiles stiffly at the young secretary, slightly embarrassed at her vivacious good humour and figure-hugging dress. She's trying not to rattle the cup on the saucer in her right hand while clasping her handbag with her left.

"Mrs. Hogan? Miss Caldwell will see you now."

The secretary marches quickly along in her high heels and shows Mary into a long, narrow office with a window at one end. A thin young woman is seated behind the desk in a smart but somewhat sombre grey suit. Her high forehead is lowered as she scans some documents in a brown folder.

"Take a seat, please," she says without looking up.

Mary places her bag on the table and waits.

"What can we do for you today, Mrs. Hogan?" the young woman asks now, raising her head. The bright blue of her eyes takes Mary by surprise. Their colour seems to dazzle in a room of faded beige. She's a pretty young thing, despite her austere appearance.

"I'm here to make a will," Mary answers.

"I see. And who will be the main beneficiaries?" the solicitor asks, scribbling away.

"Well, that's the problem really... I don't know," Mary explains.

The young woman's forehead wrinkles with confusion and just a touch of irritation. "You don't know?"

"Well I don't have any relatives you see. Except one."

"Okaaay," answers the solicitor. "And who would that be?" she questions, smiling wanly and tapping her pen on the desk.

"My daughter," she hesitates. "Katie."

"Great. Let's get it sorted then. What do you wish to bequeath?"

"No, no. You're going too fast. You see...I don't know where Katie is." Mary can tell that the young woman in front of her is wearing a thin veil over her impatience. She starts to feel panicky again, thinks about asking for a different solicitor. She even thinks about forgetting the whole thing.

"Your daughter has moved away then, has she?" the lady asks.

"No. I don't know. You see, I don't know where she lived in the first place."

The forehead is raised again and this time there is a flicker of interest.

"My daughter was adopted at birth, Miss Caldwell. I...I haven't seen her since she was five days old." Mary's voice is almost inaudible as the grief returns, like frost on autumn leaves.

"I see, Mrs Hogan. I'm sorry to hear that." The solicitor's voice has softened but there is still an edge to it too. "There are ways of tracing adopted children nowadays, but only if they want to be found," she goes on.

"That's why I'm here," Mary answers. "I thought maybe you could help with that?"

Mary is the one to look down now, too ashamed to meet the girl's blue gaze. She wants her to get on with her job; to locate her daughter and let Mary leave this world with the knowledge that at least she has given Katie something useful. She doesn't expect reunions or undying love. Just proof that she has left something behind. The solicitor makes letters dance on the page in front of her. They flurry and spin off the desk, dashing against Mary like grit. She passes over the birth certificate and confirmation of adoption to the young woman and quietly makes her way out the door.

"We'll be in touch, Mrs. Hogan," the solicitor calls after her, closing the door behind her.

Outside cars sweep fractiously along the High Street and shoppers and office workers scuttle past. Mary finds a bench and lowers herself onto it, fighting for breath. The poison of grief is slowly killing her. For so long she had lived a routine life with her husband, playing out the role of housewife and keeping their lives in order. She had never told him about her child. She had simply existed efficiently, floating in semi-detached suburbia, a living woman barely alive.

She finds the strength to get the bus home and brightens briefly at the sight of Misty waiting on the window ledge. The poor thing is nearly as old as she is and rarely leaves the house these days.

"Come on, Puss. In we go out of the cold."

The still grass of winter is cropped and short in Mary's front garden and she's glad of it. She hates having the gardener around in the spring and summer months, always babbling on and trying to talk nonsense about the weather. Of course when Jim was alive there was no need for a gardener. He happily pottered about in the garden for hours, weeding, planting, pruning away, with Mary busy in the kitchen. The distance suited them.

Mary builds up the fire again and puts the kettle on, then butters herself a couple of slices of wheaten bread. She sits down to relax and finish the jigsaw she started this morning. She doesn't like to let it sit incomplete for too long, and yet the irony of her own personal jigsaw puzzle isn't lost on her. She should have said something years ago, tried to piece it all together before now, but her father had been adamant that she tell no-one and so she kept her silence.

She's half way through her second slice of wheaten when the telephone rings. She rises slowly and goes to pick it up, scaring Misty away from under her feet.

"Hello, is that Mrs. Hogan?"

"Yes, speaking."

"It's Fiona Caldwell here from Johnston and Johnston Solicitors. I was wondering if you could call back in tomorrow?"

"So soon?"

"Yes, I'm afraid so. It's important that we iron out all the details of the adoption if we are to locate your daughter. I'll need you to take me through it."

Mary had assumed that the papers explained everything she needed to know.

"Mrs. Hogan? Mrs Hogan? Are you still there?" the voice demands.

Mary gazes out at her husband's beloved garden, watching the soil gleam in the brittle evening light. She knows she has to answer the efficient young woman on the other end of the line but she's finding it difficult. Her intention had been to leave her daughter a legacy, not to rake over old wounds with a stranger.

"Yes, dear. I'm here," her answer fractures. "What time tomorrow?"

She finds herself on the number 12 bus into town again the next morning, trying to subdue the nerves in her stomach. She passes the church where she and Jim married over 50 years ago and the little terraced house where they had lived when they first married. She passes the little primary school where she had always believed her children would go, but her marriage to Jim hadn't been blessed with children. Her punishment, of course, or at least that's how she secretly saw it. When Father Flynn told her she was doing the right thing all those years ago she had believed him. In his sleek black coat and black umbrella he was the epitome of wisdom, and her mother and father wouldn't have dared to disagree with him. Images of their servile acquiescence climb under her eyelids and she tries to blink them away.

"Sorry to drag you in again so quickly, Mrs Hogan," Fiona says, taking the old lady's coat and sitting her down to a good, strong cup of tea. The solicitor seems so much more animated this morning, Mary notices, and her eyes no longer look out of place with her clothes. She wears a pretty cornflower-blue suit and her hair is less severe, sweeping down around her shoulders.

"It's just that it's important to me to get the whole picture."

"It is?"

"Yes, Mrs. Hogan. We need details before we start searching. Now relax and tell me what you remember. Why did you put your daughter up for adoption?"

"I...I didn't think you'd need to know any of that," answers Mary, her lip visibly trembling. Nothing had penetrated her silence for 50 years and now here is this young woman expecting her to spill her heart out. The girl seems to be positively bustling with energy at this stage, so unlike the austere professional she had been the day before.

"You see I've looked over your documents, Mary, and I feel it's important for me to understand your circumstances in case your daughter, well...in case she has any questions."

"I see," Mary answers. "It's not something I've talked about before Miss Caldwell. I...I don't know where to start."

"Please, call me Fiona. And just start at the beginning."

The solicitor's hand reaches out to touch Mary's and she feels a jolt of energy. Somehow the room around her seems less faded today. Mary slowly tells the young woman her story, explaining how angry her mother and father had been and how she didn't have a choice.

"I remember the day I carried her to the station. Even the houses seemed to shiver and huddle as the rain fell," she explains. "I thought the world was coming to an end. And in a way, it was."

Fiona isn't writing anything down now, just listening intently. Her eyes dance around as if searching Mary's face.

"I handed her over at the station to one of the nuns. I thought my insides were going to fall out."

Then she stops speaking. She feels nauseous remembering the flexed waves of the Lough that day as she made her way to the station. She grew up in a village wary with gossip, and her father had been determined not to let the locals know anything about his daughter's disgrace. She feels like she is deep under water, almost feels the pressure of the Lough around her again.

"What was you father's name, Mary?"

"Patrick McBride."

"And your mother's?"

"Mary. I was named after her," she answers, puzzled at the questions. "I never realised you would need to know these kind of details," she ventures.

"As I said, Mary, we need the whole picture. Now I know this has been upsetting for you, so why don't I run you home? No point in you hanging around for another bus."

Mary decides that she must have misjudged the girl. She isn't sure how to react to her newfound gentleness but she's feeling tired and a lift home would be much easier than hauling herself on to yet another bus. She had been shocked when she looked in the mirror this morning and seen that she had lost yet more weight, making her cheekbones and forehead look even higher, almost noble. The watch Jim had bought her some years ago is loose on her wrist, her skin like paper underneath it.

Fiona kindly eases her into the car. The sun is well up and a few laggard clouds hurry across the otherwise flawless sky. Mary notices that the young solicitor drives carefully all the way back to Pinewood Avenue.

"You'll come in for a cuppa, love?"

"That would be lovely, Mary. I've cleared my diary for the afternoon so I'm in no rush."

Despite her illness Mary's house is as spotless as always and the sweet tang of furniture polish hits them as soon as they get through the door. She tells the young woman to make herself at home in the living room and is surprised to see her walk straight over to the photographs on the mantelpiece.

"Is this your wedding day?" Mary hears her call as she puts the kettle on. "Wow, you were a beauty!" the girl continues.

111

Mary has heard that said many times before but even at 74 years old, she doesn't tire of hearing it again.

"And this photograph? Are these your parents?"

"Yes, love. Stern looking, aren't they?" she almost laughs. "My father worked at the factory on Canal Street his whole life and never complained about it," she adds, falling back into reminiscence. She remembers how he'd come home, tired and reticent each evening, with only a few words for his wife and daughter.

"It's good to keep the past alive though, isn't it, Mary? Without photographs like these, how would any of us know who we are?"

Mary is surprised that Fiona is taking such an interest. She hadn't seemed like the kind of girl who would be concerned about a client's family history, but here she is cradling these old photographs carefully in her hands.

"You had no brothers or sisters?"

"No, there was just me," she answers. "Father placed all his hopes in me and I let him down."

Mary's voice is barely a whisper now, but the girl seems to catch her words. She puts her arm around the older woman and the two of them stand still for a long time, saying nothing, but understanding. The floor ripples beneath them.

"Mary, I'd like to come back and see you tomorrow, if that's OK? There's something I need to show you before we go any further."

At 10.20 the next morning Fiona Caldwell is back at Mary's door. She has a folder in her hands and an expression on her face that Mary cannot read. She makes straight for the maroon sofa in the front room and pulls papers hastily from her folder.

"Mary, I want you to look at this," she says. "Look at it really closely!" Fiona hands her an adoption certificate.

"Yes, that's Katie's. I gave you this the other day," Mary says, looking up at her, confused.

"But that's not the copy you gave me, Mary," Fiona explains slowly. "That copy belongs to someone else."

"Who? I...I don't understand, Fiona."

Mary feels her heart kick in her chest. She isn't entirely sure what the girl is trying to get at, but she senses it's important. Very important.

"That copy belongs to my mother. Katie Caldwell." The solicitor speaks slowly.

"Formerly Katie Mussen. And before that, Katie McBride."

Mary feels her ears pound as if she is under water. The pain in her chest comes back and for one single moment she thinks she can hear the distant whistle of a train. The room bleeds away and then restores itself.

"My mother was adopted by John and Kathleen Mussen, Mary. But you are her mother. You're my grandmother, Mary!"

Mary rubs at her chest. She cannot see. Fiona moves towards her and puts an arm around her shoulder. Under the girl's gaze, Mary's brimming eyes dry like summer pools. Eyes the same colour as her own reflect back at her. Her grand-daughter's.

"I'm sorry if this is too much for you. I know it's a lot to take in."

For some reason the air smells like that old familiar low tide and browned-out seaweed. Mary is transported back to that little village by the Lough and she finds herself trembling, on the verge of more tears.

"She's outside, Mary. Waiting in the car."

Many times throughout her life Mary's mind has been tired and numb. She often felt like she was watching a scene of someone else's life; someone whom she neither had sympathy nor blame for. Now her past is being handed back to her, just as her future is ebbing away. She closes her eyes and says a silent prayer, feeling the soft touch of Fiona's hand raising her gently upwards. Together they walk to the front door. Fiona opens it and Mary Hogan's silence slips away.

Her daughter Katie reaches out to her and cradles her like a long lost child.

AUNT MAGGIE

A MEMORY BY A.E. WREN
Pontefract, Great Britain

When Mary visits Aunt Maggie, she brings with her wonderful news.

" Aunt Maggie! It's me," I shouted, leaning my bike up against the wall. Her yellow door was open at the top. Reaching over I unlatched the bottom half and walked in."Maggie, I've some wonderful news for you," I said, pushing my headscarf back. I still had a trace of my local accent then, despite my time in England. Walking through to the back I saw her scattering meal for the chickens, her reedy voice serenading them.

"Mary Kathleen Harrahy. Where've you been these past months?" I gave her tiny frame a hug. Taking her arm I led her into the house. "You'll be stopping for tea, then?" She took her customary place in the rocking chair by the fire whilst I filled the kettle and put it on the range.

"Maggie, I'm getting married." Even now I can see the absolute amazement on her face.

"Married! You're far too young to be getting married. You're still at your schooling."

"I'm twenty-four! I finished my teacher-training two years ago. It's time I was married." Pouring us both a cup of tea I told her everything.

"Tell me when?"

"My birthday."

"St. Patrick's Day?" I nodded. "That was the day my Michael died in France all those years ago." A tear came into her eye. It was decades before I understood that she saw in me the embodiment of her own lost hopes.

"Well," she said at last, "you'll be needing a bottom drawer, a dress and I've just the thing for you." Disappearing into the

114

next room, she came back with a parcel and carefully folded back the tissue paper to reveal a bolt of white cloth and some lace.

"Mammy and me worked hard for this. Saving every penny until we could go to Tubbercurry to buy it. I've no use for it myself. But I thought it might be gracious enough for you and your Michael."

I protested – her gift was too precious. She was adamant and in the end I accepted. She told me how she and her mother had planned to make her own dress, embroidering it with flowers and shamrock.

"Mammy was to leave a pocket in the hem to be sewn up on the morning of my wedding day with a real shamrock leaf inside," she said. But her day had never come. She never asked me to do the same, but I knew it was what she wanted. So, that morning in March 1953 I thought of her as I put the final stitch into the hem of my dress.

I didn't go back to Muckelty until 1959. My son was five, my daughter three. It was the middle of March. Odd how the same dates seem to crop up at significant points during a lifetime. Maggie must have been almost 70 by then. No one in the family really knew how old she was. I'm not so sure she knew herself. Then, her yellow door was faded with signs of rot at the bottom corner.

"Maggie," I said.

She was in her chair by the fire. Struggling to her feet, her blue eyes filled with tears. "Mary! You're back at last."

"Didn't you get my letter?"

"Aye, but I can't always make out the words these days and who is this little man here?"

"Michael John, your great-nephew. This is Little Maggie. She's named after you," I said introducing my sleeping daughter.

"Well. Would you look at them both! And don't you look grand, Mary."

When my daughter awoke, Maggie sat her on her knee and with Michael at her feet she was telling the same stories she told me when I was a girl. Her voice had become unsteady and quieter. Her once jet-black hair was completely grey but still tied in a bun at the back of her neck as it always had been. I stayed a week that year, little understanding the portent of each precious moment.

"Now you'll not be taking so long to come back and see me, will you, Mary?" she said as we were leaving.

In England, March disappeared, April slid into May and that summer I became pregnant again. We couldn't afford another trip, but I kept writing and sending photographs. Cards at Christmas and birthdays would arrive with a barely readable message, envelopes addressed in a different, more expert hand. Always the same message, "I'm grand, Mary. Love Maggie."

In March 1963, our parish priest came to tell me that Maggie had "passed away" on the 17th.

After the funeral I stood once again outside that yellow door. She had very little. In a drawer in her bedroom I found my letters lovingly preserved, an old photograph of a soldier and the post she had received from the Western Front. I've still got them, even now.

A fat

"Not even a bill?"

"You can have mine. I'm not sh…

Pete smiled, "The kettle is aft…

"Good stuff."

"So," Pete said and then b…
to say.

The postman was an…
away. In his youth he…
those days most run…
say it was an acc…
regard the spike…
muscles were…
two sons, Lu…
Scound…
want to…
disapp…
So…
on…

C wincing
him. Las
floods ha
submerged
the wooden
brought up anyth…
Mud coloured river water
spilled over the rims of his welling…
his neighbours trying to save their few
never experienced flooding. Not in the whole o…
and when the flood waters receded, it wasn't too long befo…
hard frost came and then the snow. He had known winters like
it, of course, but he had forgotten about how bad they used to
be. How the snow served as nature's prison bars and confined
people to their homes.

He lived at the end of a bohereen that had a thick beard of
grass straddling two shallow tyre ruts. He owned a red van he
no longer had the courage to drive and Lucy was, he realised,
the last dog that he would bury. His cottage in which he had
reared two sons by himself, having lost Mary young, had a head
of dirty brown thatch and freshly whitewashed walls with sills
of green trim. All recently painted by his sons who had arrived
for a fortnight in June to torment him.

"Tom, morning to you. Anything for me?" Pete asked.

"Not even a flier."

rt of those."

r boiling."

oke off for lack of something else

O'Rourke from the village two miles
won a national cross-country race. In
ers ran barefooted, one who didn't...they
dent and Tom himself believed so. In any
tore down along his calf and afterwards the
ever the same. He was best friends with Pete's
ke and Mattie.

els, the pair of them, Pete thought. They wouldn't
darken his door again. If ever a man had sons who'd
inted him beyond measure, well he was the man.
mething's not right with Tom, Pete thought. He had a face
him like a man after being tasked with a job that he believed
was beyond him.

"There's a harsh change in the air," Tom said as he crossed
the threshold ahead of Pete. Lucy had taken to resting herself on
the third stair to the attic; the poor craytur would never forget
the watery nightmare. Sometimes at night she whimpered in
her sleep.

"Tis."

"The May trees are leaning to the east," Tom said, sitting in
the green easy chair by the black stove that Pete had lit an hour
ago.

"A sign of bad weather, so," Pete said. He added, "Sure it
can't be much worse than last year."

"It wouldn't want to be, for my bones are still drying out."

"Don't talk to me about bones. I got a new creak and a terrible
dart of pain this morning. In my knees, would you believe and
me with the soundest legs all my life."

"The arthritis," Tom said.

"The arthritis," Pete lamented.

Tom mentioned how his mother had been an Irish dancer in her young days, winning all Ireland medals galore, "...but jay she's suffering with bad toes now."

"A grand woman."

Mrs. O'Rourke had been Pete's neighbour until a few years ago when she sold up the parcel of land and the two storey house and went to live with Tom's sister.

"She wouldn't have stuck the floods," Tom said, "she'd have moved to high ground and stayed there."

"We all would do, I suppose, if we had the means."

"Means or no, a person has to think of his health."

"Aye...health."

Silence.

Pete sipped at his tea, a long drawn out slurp, as though he were drawing from a well of thoughts.

"Have you heard any word from the lads?" Tom asked quietly.

"Any word from them? I'm deaf to whatever that pair would have to say."

"I couldn't blame you," Tom said, his grey eyes fixed on the steam rising from his mug.

"Could you not?"

"No. I'm glad my lads aren't like them."

Pete's chin climbed a few inches. He rubbed at the whiskers that had escaped his razor's blade. Tom was a friend to both of his lads. Had he seen through them, too?

"Nice lads now; don't get me wrong," Tom said, "But..."

"But what?"

Tom bit on his lower lip, shook his head, looked into his tea like it was the veritable cup of poison.

"Tom?" Pete prompted.

"Don't mind me, Pete. It's not my place to speak ill of a friend's sons."

"They're your friends, too."

"So they are, but it's not something I'd boast of, not anymore. There was a time that..." Tom pointed at a box on the pine table and asked Pete if he was going to open it.

"No."

"Why not?"

"The lads bought it for me. Wasters."

"It's the least they could do for you."

Putting his mug on the hearth, Tom went over to the table and slid the box this way and that on the table, reading the labels.

"A cheap old thing," he said.

"Is it?"

"About 300 hundred euros is all it cost."

Pete wasn't sure if he had heard right. Three hundred euros? Cheap? Ah, my hearing must be shot, he thought.

"There's a camera in it," Tom said.

"A camera phone."

"Cheap, like I said."

"How many euros did you say it cost?"

Tom said the price with mild disdain that Pete knew was not genuine.

"Hmm."

"Your old phone was better."

The one that had fallen from his hand into the flood waters.

"It was. Mattie took the sam card out and said..."

"Sim card."

"Anyhow I have it there in the press and do you know what else he said?"

Tom didn't answer.

"He said I'd have all my own numbers on my new phone."

"He's right...they'll all be saved on it."

"I see."

"So, he wasn't lying to you that time."

Pete's eyes followed Tom as he returned to his chair. Watched him as he opened the door to the stove and added in turf.

"Mattie's not a liar," he said.

"I didn't say he was."

"Neither is Luke."

"I never said that they were, Pete."

"You said he wasn't lying that time...that means you must think he told a lie *sometime*."

A frown dug itself a niche across Tom's broad forehead. He shook his head and then clicked his fingers, "...I have his lie now."

"Tell me what he said."

Outside the sun shone through a burst of rain. Lucy hurried to Pete and sat at his feet.

"Luke said that himself and Mattie had built a granny flat for you at the rear of Mattie's garden and that you wouldn't even look at it. Sure I know that's an awful lie; they're ashamed of having left their father to rot in the floods and the snow and are trying to save face with people. I know you, Pete, and you're a man of integrity and would have an appreciation of the things that people do to help. 'Go on away from me, Mattie and Luke,' I said, 'you're a pair of curs."

"What man would live in a granny flat?"

"Indeed."

"This is my home."

"And it's here that you must stay, Pete. They should respect your wishes."

"They should."

Bowsies, Pete thought, trying to coerce me into abandoning the family home. Here I was born, here I laid out Mary and it's here I'll die. How could I carry a crowd of memories from here to anywhere else?

"I saw the...I can't even bring myself to describe what they built for you. I wouldn't put a pig in it," Tom said.

"A right shack, no doubt," Pete said.

"A large bedroom, sitting room, kitchen and bathroom, a new stove...fenced off from the main house...shutting you away down at the end of the garden; probably told you you'd have great privacy, I bet. And a bit of a garden for you to look after."

Exactly. Said the flat had its own driveway, too, Pete remembered. "What did you say to them?" Pete asked.

"I said they had hard necks."

"Did you?"

"I did."

"Good for you."

Pete himself had told the pair to get out the door and not to sully the air around here with their presence ever again. Oh, and the Luke lad with his mother's cross face said he lacked appreciation.

"For sure it's here that I'll stay."

"Why wouldn't you? This is your home, you've a history here, my God. Why would you leave?"

Pete said, "Your mother, did you encourage her to leave?"

Tom said quietly but measured, "I did. And also she said she was getting too old and didn't want to live in a remote place. That it wasn't fair on us."

"On ye?"

"She didn't want us worrying about her. She's glad she didn't remain on; she'd have been washed out of it like yourself and that's no joke. The woman is ninety-two this year. Wasn't she good to be so considerate toward us?"

"She was and yet you think the opposite of me. How is that?"

Tom shook his head, "You're a man, Pete, it's different for a man."

Pete couldn't balance the logic. His sons would worry about him just as much as Tom and his sister would worry about their mother. Gender didn't factor in.

"You'll be well able for the hard weather; get in plenty of fuel, get yourself a gas heater in the loft. Have in a store of food... you'll be grand. And the reek of the place has improved."

The smell of last year's winter clung to the walls. Of must, of damp – there were large damp patches on the wall – mildew, a pastiche of stains. The odour reminded him of an old shed he had once entered. It had been locked up for years and was home to dozens of pigeons. He had gagged and retched.

"It's like a faint smell of rotten eggs," Tom said.

"You're honest, Tom, I give you that."

"It's Lucy I feel sorry for – she's terrified."

"She is not."

"She is. When she heard the rain, what did she do?"

Pete nodded and reached down and stroked her coat.

"As for that Luke fella's idea," Tom said.

"What idea did he say to you?"

Tom said that Luke told him his father could have moved back into the house during the summer months.

"Does he think you're a film star, moving from a summer house to a winter house? I don't know what you fed those boys when they were growing up, but it wasn't good for them."

Pete looked long, hard and sharp at his friend and smiled. He saw his sons' last ditch effort coming through in him. "Do you think I'm downright stupid?"

"What?"

"Errah, I know what you're at; I'll move out during winter. For my sake, for the sake of my lads and the poor dog. But mostly for you, you jennet."

"For me?"

Pete said there was nothing worse than having to sit listening to a postman spin reverse psychology. "Would you unwrap that phone while I go get my sam card?"

Tom sighed relief.

"And don't tell me its proper name, Tom, you've spun enough guff for the day."

GOING BACK

By BARBARA DYNES

Poole, Dorset, England

When Kate returns to Northern Ireland after being away from there for 40 years, it brings back painful memories but also a chance to resolve the past.

Going down to her hotel breakfast on her first morning in Northern Ireland, Kate felt odd. The phrase "a stranger in a strange land" went through her mind as she ordered. The family at the next table – mum, dad and little boy - smiled at her.

"Nice, sunny day!" the lady said. "On holiday, love?"

"Yes," Kate answered.

You could call it a holiday, she supposed – a holiday with a purpose. Though, 40 years ago, this had been her home.

"We've come over for my friend's wedding," the woman went on. "It's later today - here in the hotel–"

"Tomorrow we're going to The Giant's Causeway," the lad broke in excitedly. "D'you know, a real giant once walked right across the sea on the stones!"

"Really?" Kate laughed. "How exciting!"

"So friendly, the Irish, after all they've been through," the man said, shaking his head. "Difficult to believe the Troubles ever happened."

Kate's smile faded. Oh, they happened all right. Every shocking episode, every nasty twist and turn, every grim newspaper item was evidence. Back in England, though, throughout those years, she'd watched folk frown, shake their heads, acknowledge the horror of it all, then get on with their lives. What was going on just across the Irish Sea might have been thousands of miles away. Until the atrocities began in England.

The waiter, appearing with her breakfast, thankfully prevented Kate from having to answer.

Maybe she, too, could do some holiday things tomorrow - explore the Belfast shops, revisit the Mountains of Mourne, or walk around Loch Neagh. Growing up in the '60s and living "out in the sticks" so to speak, she had not ventured far. In those days you were cautious about visiting certain dangerous areas involved in the Troubles. You mostly stayed put – safe, hopefully, within your own community.

Kate shuddered and pushed away her plate. She wasn't that hungry, after all. Too much on her mind. She drank her coffee, then stood up and smiled at the English family.

"Enjoy the wedding!"

Back in her room, she put on her jacket and picked up her car keys. Time to set out. Thank goodness for her sat-nav; vague memories of the Portadown area would not get her far. Anyway, there was no hurry. She had waited years for this day, she didn't want to rush things. That was one of the reasons she had decided to take the ferry across. To give herself time to think.

Tom, her son, thought she was mad. "Flying's so much quicker – hire a car when you get there!" he'd said on the phone. He had no inkling of her real reason for coming here. He thought it was to look up old haunts, see how things had changed. Dear old Mum, wallowing in nostalgia and all that. Little did he know she was on a mission.

Yet Tom was well aware of the family history. But he'd not mentioned it on the phone - and why should he? Tom represented another generation, another era. Mind you, she had braced herself in case the subject of his Uncle Bill, whom he'd never met, came up. Fiercely patriotic Bill, Kate's only brother, would never ever leave Ireland, especially now their parents had died. Bill was the family's only remaining link with the country. Bill..."Forget him!" Jack, her ex-husband, used to say.

Kate frowned. Life with Jack, before the messy divorce, was once quite magical. In those early days, when Tom was little, she'd still believed in that giant walking across the Causeway, leprechauns and suchlike, even though she was living in England. Not now. She'd come to Northern Ireland to lay ghosts, rather than stalk giants.

Later, driving through Portadown, Kate felt really tense. Stopping at the florist's earlier, to buy the bouquet of red roses lying on the passenger seat, had really brought home to her what she was doing. She glanced out of the window at the crowds. Strange to think that this was once home. And still home to Bill, of course. Sometimes she thought she recognised odd landmarks, yet everything seemed so different, so much brighter!

"No police, no soldiers, Kate," she told herself. There was more life, more optimism everywhere, in spite of the recession. People were smiling. That man at breakfast had been right. Life here had moved on, sure it had. She grinned. Easy to lapse back into the Irish idiom!

When her sat-nav told her that she had reached her destination, Kate pulled in at a lay-by. She took a deep breath. This was a Catholic area and, way back, it would have been awash with flags, each coloured green, white and orange. In Protestant districts the union flags had flown just as proudly. Forty years ago she, a Protestant, had rarely set foot in some Catholic places. You just didn't; just as Catholics, in turn, kept away from Protestant areas. That was what it was all about.

She got out of the car. A crowd of young people, grinning and shouting, stepped into the road to make way for her on the pavement. Kate smiled at them, wondering. How much of the Troubles did they remember? Had bad things happened to their families? It was surely going to take years to wipe out all antagonism here.

She suddenly stopped. There, in front of her, was the cemetery - exactly as she remembered it, with massive oak trees and numerous headstones. Seeming to be on automatic pilot, she made for the far corner...and Terry's grave.

It was well tended, the grass atop it neatly cut. A stone angel had been erected by the family and she felt a lump in her throat as she gazed at the headstone:

Terry O'Brien
Born June 4ᵗʰ 1950
Killed Oct.15ᵗʰ 1972
Aged 22 Years

May He Rest In Peace

Kate, suddenly feeling quite weak, sank down on to the gravel path. This, then, was it! She had been dreaming for years of coming back to her beloved Terry's grave. She could hardly believe she was here. But first things first - the flowers. Over by the water tap lay several old glass jars. Filling one with water, she put the roses inside and placed them on the grave. Then, sitting back on her heels, she blinked at the vivid contrast of colour – the red on the bright green. Symbolic...splashes of blood on Ireland's soil.

"Don't be so dramatic, Kate!" she murmured. Nonetheless, her eyes filled with tears as she pictured her Terry as she remembered him. The scruffy, long blond hair...the tall angular body...and those laughing, blue Irish eyes.

Then she saw herself - an innocent 20 year old, far too trusting, never dreaming that underneath Terry's light-hearted banter lay a serious side, an involvement with things so much darker. Things she didn't understand, any more than she understood her brother, Bill. Whoever would have thought that he.... She closed her eyes.

Bill and Terry had hated each other. Well, at least she understood that part of it. And the other thing she had quickly realised was that it couldn't last, her love affair with Terry. A Catholic and a Proddie, no way! When she'd said the same to Terry he had just held her tight, told her he loved her and added,

"One day it will all be over, you'll see. Which is why people have to act now, to make sure of that."

Kate shivered and hugged her knees. It had been pitch dark that night, the night Terry's family had come to their house, looking for Bill.

"Our Billy's not here," her terrified mother had shouted through the closed door.

"No? Then we'll find him, you bet! Your lad's shot and killed our Terry!"

Kate kicked at a stone. She would never forget those terrible words, yelled by Sean, Terry's brother. She remembered, too, the sick feeling, the numb disbelief as she and her hysterical mother hugged each other.

"I don't believe it!" Mum had wailed. "Our Billy would never..."

But it was true. Kate bit her lip. There had been far more behind the tragedy; her falling in love with a Catholic was only part of the story. She recalled the pain, the grief...and a defiant, stubborn Bill getting put away for years. Leaving for England and a teaching job soon after he was sentenced, she had never spoken to him again.

Kate stared at the name "Terry". Had she loved him more than she'd loved Jack - the man she eventually married? Possibly. Yet she and Terry had been so young. Would they...could they have found a way to stay together? Probably not, in that climate. As for Bill...now out of prison, her brother was still trying to contact her with letters full of remorse. At birthdays, Christmas, the births of his own children – any excuse. Bill had never given up. She just destroyed everything he sent.

Kate stood up. She had done what she'd come here to do, yet she still felt unsettled. She'd hoped for some kind of closure. Maybe that was impossible. She stroked the cold grey headstone.

"Bye, Terry," she whispered.

Suddenly very tired, she turned and walked back to her car.

Later, at the hotel, she ordered some sandwiches and, feeling in need of company, sat in the bar. Tom texted her. She replied that she was having a marvellous time, "great food, great company". She grinned ruefully. The great food was a cheese sandwich and the company a few giggling, formally-dressed people, who had obviously strayed in from the wedding the family at breakfast had mentioned.

"Phew! It's so hot in there!" A middle-aged man, dressed in lilac tie and full wedding gear, sank into a chair next to her.

"Wedding go OK?" Kate smiled, eager to lighten her mood.

"Great!" he replied. "My daughter's married a smashing lad and I managed to pull off some kind of speech. People actually laughed, sure they did!"

Kate laughed. His strong Northern Irish accent reminded her of her father's voice from way back.

"Good!" she said. "Have they known each other long, the happy couple?"

"Four years, so it is." He leaned forward, a serious expression on his flushed face. "You know," he went on, "a few years ago this weddin' would have caused a big division within the family."

"Really?"

"Yes. Different religions, see. My Maria's Catholic. Declan's not."

"Oh!" Kate was suddenly tongue-tied.

"But we all get along fine! Times they are a changin'!" He grinned and stood up. "Better get back. Bye!"

"All the best!" Kate said.

She sat there for a long time, thinking hard. Fate was a curious thing – had she, Bill and Terry been born a few decades later, life would surely have taken a different, less awful turn. "One day it will all be over..." Terry's words. Well, the changes here were, in part, what her Terry had yearned for. There might have been a few glitches in the quest for peace, but there was a definite lack of tension on the streets and, thankfully, more understanding between people.

Kate suddenly realised what she had to do. Tomorrow she would give the holiday jaunts a miss. There was another important mission to undertake; a visit to someone that was long overdue. The outcome of that journey would surely give her the closure she needed. And she had a feeling that meeting Bill might prove to be even more magical than catching sight of a giant striding across the sea.

THE DOLL AND PRAM

A memory by DORA SCOTT

Newtownabbey, Co. Antrim

*A special Christmas present helps one little girl in recovering from
pneumonia.*

In the winter of 1953 when I was six years old, I was very
ill with pneumonia. My parents were told that there was
a good chance that I would not survive. I required 24
hour nursing care that was willingly given by my distracted
mother and hard working father.

My aunts and uncles were regular visitors. I remember Aunt
Cissie, my mother's sister, bringing me a bottle of Lucozade
and a little dress that she had made for my favourite doll.
Auntie Peggy, my great aunt, called with sweets and a brand
new album of stories. Other aunts and uncles called, all with
the same concerned look on their faces.

Gradually I became stronger and was allowed to get up for a
short time each day, then back to bed to read one of my many
books and comics, lovingly given by my anguished extended
family.

Taking medicine was no joke and I remember almost being
sick as the horrible liquids ran down the back of my throat.
Mummy bribed me by telling me that Santa had heard about
me and that he was going to bring a special present.

The first day that I was taken outside for a little walk, my
poor spindly legs could hardly carry me. Mummy said that she
was going to write to Santa and tell him how hard I was trying
to get better.

As Christmas approached, there was no attendance by me
at the usual round of parties. I wasn't strong enough to go
anywhere.

I remember my sister waking me on Christmas morning
to tell me that Santa had been at our house and had left us

presents. There beside my bed was the grandest doll's pram and a big baby dolly sleeping gently inside.

Among my other presents were two fancy pram covers and frilly pillowcases to match. One set was white satin with a big bow and lace on the pillowcase made by our next door neighbour, Mrs. McFadyen and the other was green with little flowers lovingly stitched and quilted by Aunt Cissie. There were a couple of little cardigans and two dresses all for my baby doll, later named Carol as she had been born at Christmas.

The pram was coach built, a junior Silver Cross and in later years I was told that mummy and daddy had paid it at £1 a week before Christmas. Daddy had worked lots of overtime in order to pay the enormous sum of money that was twice the amount of his weekly wage.

Mary, my sister, got a watch from Santa and a few bits and pieces, not much in comparison to my elaborate present. She didn't show any envy or resentment at the imbalance. When we grew up she told me that she had been part of the secret and it made her feel grown up, and this pleased her more than presents.

When I think of that Christmas I get quite emotional; my mummy and daddy who were out of their minds with worry over my health and were determined to make it a Christmas to remember. They succeeded as it was one that I will never forget. I am sure that daddy never forgot either; he was supposed to get a new overcoat but had to "make do" with one of granda's that was altered and had new buttons sewn on so that it fitted him.

Memories can be more valuable than gold.

ALMOST TOMORROW

BY JOAN SKURA
Toronto, Ontario, Canada

While waiting for her husband to return from the war, Claire receives some shocking news.

With the morning rush over, Claire Harrington wiped down the marble-topped counter at McBride's Grocery and Fine Meats and went to the window to look out on Rampart Street. The town of New Rothsay, Ontario, was abuzz, preparations for the returning troops in full swing. Strings of tiny Union Jacks had been hung over the thoroughfare and, at every intersection, a huge banner had been hoisted, each with a different message of pride and welcome.

"Busy morning, eh?" Alec McBride finished cleaning the bacon slicer and joined her at the window. "Those ladies must've used up just about all their food coupons for the month in one go. Aye, but who could blame them? It's not every day you get to welcome home a husband or a son. Town's goin' all out on this bash."

"Yes," Claire murmured. "Tomorrow's a big day for everyone."

"Why don't you head on home, Claire? You must have lots to do. And don't worry, Maggie will fill in 'til you're ready to come back—that is if Frank's willin' to let you out of his sight once he's home." Alec laughed heartily. Claire managed a smile.

"Oh, I don't really need to-"

"No, no, I insist."

"Well, OK. Thanks, Mr. McBride."

Claire went to the wall telephone and dialled her mother's number. "Hi, Mom, I'm leaving a little early today. Could you have Beth ready, please?"

"Oh, sure. Claire, dear...about tomorrow..."

"Mom, I can't talk now. See you soon. Bye."

She hung up and went to the storeroom in the back, aware that Alec was studying her. As she took the gold-coloured compact and lipstick case from her purse, she thought about the morning, women laughing, bubbling over with anticipation while she and Alec served them.

"Can't wait to see Sam tomorrow, Mr. McBride. On second thought, make that two dozen eggs and a pound of cheddar."

"You ladies are as excited as kids waitin' for Santa Claus."

"Oh, Claire, I was so afraid something terrible would happen to Jack. You must have been worried about Frank, too."

"Yes...yes, I was worried. Is that everything on your list, Betty?"

"Isn't it awful about Charlie Endicott? Poor Sally, I feel so bad. Don't know what to say to her these days."

"Yes...it's awful. Anything else today, Millie?"

"It'll be just like a second honeymoon, girls!"

"Oh, leave it to Alice to think of nothing but that, huh, Claire?"

And so it went.

But, for Claire, these last three years had been a relief; the overseas posting a godsend and now he was coming home. It would all begin again. Oh Lord, that last time, the week before he shipped out, she'd had Mom drive her all the way to the hospital in Kerrsville. She could still hear the doctor's words as he stitched the gash above her eye.

"Mrs. Harrington, this isn't the first time you've been here. I urge you to tell someone, before..."

No, no, she'd protested. He'd be overseas in a week; she'd be fine.

Claire secured her hat with the pearl hatpin and put on her plaid coat. The powder and lipstick had done their work, she thought, lending a rosier glow to her pale skin.

She walked along Rampart Street, past little knots of townspeople adding finishing touches to decorations, washing store windows. She nodded at each greeting.

"Afternoon, Claire. Big day for you tomorrow, eh?"

"Won't it be nice for you and Frank and little Beth to be a family again?"

At Myrlene's Beauty Shop, she stopped and looked through the window. Her best friend, Vera, scissors in hand, caught sight of her and motioned for her to wait. She saw Vera lean forward and say something to the customer, who nodded.

"Whew, what a day. We've been run off our feet." Vera closed the door and ran her fingers, comblike, through her dark curls. "They all want to look pretty for hubby." She looked at Claire. "You finished early, I see. How're you doing?"

"Alec gave me the rest of the day off. He's got Maggie filling in 'til I can come back. I didn't have the heart to tell him I don't want any time off. But Frank will go crazy if he knows I'm working full-time; he thinks it's still two days a week."

"Gee, Claire, maybe you should just come out with it tomorrow, tell him you've gone full-time. Hell, he's the reason you've had to. Damn him, withholding money like that! And from his own child, too. When's the last time you had anything from him? It's a disgrace!"

"Oh, what would I do without you, Vee?" Claire hugged her. "But you'd better get back inside. Mrs. Thompson's looking a little anxious."

"OK, take it easy, kiddo."

Claire turned off Rampart onto Chestnut, crossed the leaf-covered street and walked through Queen Mary's Park. Away from the main drag it was quiet; the only sounds were the scrunching of leaves underfoot and the chattering of a squad of squirrels as they chased each other through the maples. The mid-October sun was warm and Claire sat on a bench.

Vera was right, she should tell him straightaway. There'd been nothing for over a year. No money, letters. For all she knew, he could be...but no, they'd have notified her. Just like poor Sally Endicott. She shuddered. No, she didn't want that. But how did he think she was going to look after a three year-old, pay the rent, bills? Sure, he knew about McBride's two days a week, but how far would that go? Well, knowing Frank, he'd expect her to give up the little apartment over the bookstore and go live at her mother's and it had almost come to that. And then Maggie McBride came down with pneumonia and had to quit the store. When Alec offered the full-time job, Claire had jumped at the chance.

Why hadn't Frank answered any of her letters this past year? Not even a card for Beth's birthday. And why had he stopped the bank deposits? She'd been forced to write to the military, asking if there'd been some mistake, an oversight, perhaps. And oh, the humiliating response, no mistake; it was her husband's wish that the deposits cease. She winced at the memory, hugging her purse tight against her. Then she rose and continued through the park and out onto Stirling Avenue. Her mother's bungalow sat at the end of the street and she quickened her pace, eager to see Beth.

In the hallway, Claire slipped off her shoes, hat and coat and smoothed her tawny, shoulder-length hair. The sweetness of fresh baking reached her.

"Mommy, Mommy; me and Gramma made cupcakes. Come see."

Laughing, Claire kissed Beth's warm little cheek and allowed herself to be dragged into the kitchen.

"Oh my, don't those look delicious. How are you, Mom? Has she run you ragged?"

"Not in the least. My Bethie's never any trouble, you know that. But how are you doing?"

Claire shook her head. "I don't know. I...I feel all mixed up. It's like I almost wish V-E Day hadn't happened. Isn't that dreadful of me? Sally Endicott and so many others will never see their men again and mine is coming home." She blinked away the tears before Beth could see them. "Mmm...those cupcakes look good; let's have one before we go. What goes with cupcakes, I wonder?"

"Milk!" crowed Beth.

"Milk, of course. Now, you sit in your chair and I'll get your glass. Would you like some tea, Mom?"

"That would be grand." Peg switched on the radio and sat down at the kitchen table. An announcer was saying,

"And now, it's the forces' sweetheart, Miss Vera Lynn, singing 'We'll Meet Again'."

Peg looked at Claire. "Shall I turn it off?"

"No, it's OK, Mom."

The kettle whistled as the doorbell rang. Peg rose to answer it.

"Hi Peg, is Claire here?" It was Barney Stubbs, the mailman.

"Yes, she's in the kitchen. Come on in. Would you like some tea?"

"Oh, no thanks, I just came to give this letter to...oh, there you are, Claire."

"What is it, Barney?" Claire said.

"Well, it's this letter from overseas. Only it wasn't in time for this morning's delivery and I didn't want to wait for tomorrow's, so I brought it 'round to the store, but Mr. McBride says, 'She left early today; you'll probably catch her at her mother's place', so I brought it here." He paused for breath. "The postmark says August the twelfth. It just came in today. I'm real sorry, Claire."

"It's OK; it's not your fault. And thank you for bringing it. Are you sure you won't have some tea?"

"No, really, I gotta go. The missus has me runnin' all sorts of errands, what with our Danny home tomorrow. You know how it is."

"Yes, of course. Thanks again, Barney. I appreciate it."

"You're welcome. Afternoon, Peg."

Claire turned the envelope over several times. It was from Frank, all right, written two months earlier. With her thumbnail, she began to slit it open, then stopped abruptly and set it on the top shelf of the corner cabinet, propped behind a China figurine. Peg looked at her, eyebrows raised, but said nothing.

"It can wait," said Claire. "Right now, we've got cupcakes to sample." She hugged Beth, who giggled and bounced up and down in anticipation. "OK, here's your milk, honey, and Gramma's tea. Mmm...these are yummy...you two make the best."

Claire washed the dishes and tidied the kitchen, while her mother and Beth sat in the big armchair in the living room, reading a story. She took the envelope down and held it for a moment before ripping it open. A single page, written on both sides, it didn't take long to read. Claire gasped and the paper fell to the floor.

"Oh, my God," she breathed, bracing herself against a chair. She picked up the letter and placed it firmly on the kitchen table, her hands too shaky to hold it steady. She read it again — the words appearing magnified: "...not coming home...met someone over here...child, a boy, born April...."

Claire walked into the living room. "Beth, honey," she said, "go get your dolly and your books. And put on your shoes, please." She handed the letter to Peg.

"Oh, Lord. I don't believe it. How could he do this to you? If your father were alive, he'd...you can't go home now. Stay here tonight. Claire...?"

Claire gazed at her, as if from a distance. He wasn't coming back. She was free, free of him...an end to the rage. But he had someone else. And a child, as well. He'd betrayed her, betrayed Beth. The bastard! She took a deep breath.

"No, I need to go home, Mom," she said, "There are things to be done. Tomorrow's a big day."

"You're not serious. After what he's done to you? You don't have to face people just yet."

"That's exactly what I have to do. Frank's made his choice. But my life is here and I'll probably see the same folks every day. I'll start by telling Vera and Alec; then I'm going to the parade, Mom...for the others. We owe men like Charlie Endicott."

Peg nodded and embraced her. "Your father would be so proud of you," she said, her eyes misty as she looked at the sepia picture on the mantel of the young husband who had perished all those years ago in a Belgian trench.

He Was Gone With the Last of the February Frost

A *memory by* LISA KEEGAN
Sutton, Dublin 13

A woman recalls her grandfather's death.

I was met with warm weathered hands that belonged to those sad soft faces from the mountains. They had come in droves to say goodbye and now the small room smelled of turf, sweat and sheep. It was quiet and bright in the little funeral home on the hill; outside the night came in and the mourners came still. I felt forgotten for an instant in the hum of people but then in a gap between two strong country men I saw him, my grandfather lying in the open casket.

As I approached him, I was four years old again, standing in the master bedroom of the big white house. The knees of my dungarees brown from digging in the garden. I'm standing beside the French doors that lead into the conservatory; the glass castle where sunny days were spent with my grandfather in the old green sun chairs - talking but sometimes not. Sitting in that comfortable silence – the kind of safe silence I felt in his presence. The sun is shining in through the open doors past all the glass and greenery to the bedroom where I watch him sleeping. I am a wee Lilliputian and he, Gulliver - a sleeping giant on a blanket of mountains. He is the Pope, Santa Claus, God Almighty himself all at once and all in front of me. I see his eyes flutter under the thin papery veil of his eyelids and briefly wonder if Granddads dream at all and if they do, what on earth would they dream of? I imagine that it is most likely of sheep, pipes and Celtic winning the Olympics or whatever it is that football teams win. I'm on a mission this Saturday morning: I have been sent by my grandmother to bring my grandfather breakfast in bed – toast and orange juice on the old silver tray held unsteadily in my clumsy little hands. This morning breaks the dawn of a new era. I now have responsibility. I have never been given this task before; it was usually left up to the older sister who at that moment is upstairs in the big white house, nursing a broken arm. I smile to myself, now I am the only one with two perfectly functioning arms.

So as not to disturb my own personal Gulliver, I place the tray as quietly as possible on the bedside locker and then open the broadsheet I have tucked under my arm. I hold my breath as the pages crinkle, keeping an eye on my grandfather for any change in his breathing. I hoist myself onto the bed which squeaks and groans, completely undoing my cautious attempts at silence. I lay the newspaper on his chest. I squirm off the bed, brimming with satisfaction. I pull a flattened daffodil from my dungarees pocket and place it by my grandfather's hand – the strong brown hand with thick veins like blue rivers that holds mine when we walk slowly down the bohereen and sticks my pictures on the fridge. Hands browned from his times in foreign lands that I could not fathom, places I had not seen except in the stories he told me and in the treasures he returned home with: the marble elephants on the mantelpiece, the African headdress and the antelope skin on the wall.

I looked at my grandfather lying there among the people both familiar and unfamiliar. He looked small and alone in the crowded room. I kissed his forehead and walked away. Later we meandered through the narrow streets, following the hearse lit by the fluorescent lights of the shops and everything seemed to be moving so slowly. In the big church the priest talked and I could see the dust orbiting around him like a miniscule universe and I don't remember much else. And I knew the next morning we would go to the graveyard that clings to the mountainside. The mountainside which seemed to be wrapped around the earth and the wind would whip around us. The air would smell of pine cones and grief. It would be damp and the ground unstable. We would put my grandfather into the ground and that would be that. He would be gone.

But he is still alive, yes, in the smell of his aftershave and scent of his shampoo. In the early hours of the winter morning when the small robin comes to the window to greet him – even though he is not there, he is still alive, yes. And his spirit is still in the dewy grass beside the big house. Among the apples that flourish on the white trees in spring. I feel him on the bohereen after dark and the darkness and emptiness tell me that, yes, he is still alive. His cane in the cupboard under the stairs tells me that he is here, that he once walked with the help of it, it was part of him. It still exists so he still exists. In the dogs barking far away and even further away on the white sands of some unfamiliar beach where he once walked, among the palm and coconut trees, luscious life around and in him - he is still alive.

So when the telephone broke the silence of a grey Tuesday morning and through the blurry sharpness that comes from being woken suddenly, I heard my father ask urgently, "So is he gone? Is he gone?" As if in that moment if my grandfather was gone that urgency may suddenly bring him home, I knew he was not really gone.

It took me a while to find him and at first I thought I would in the photographs around the big white house and although they hold his face and grace, I could not see him in them. Sometimes if I tried to remember him too much, all that would come would be the smell of disinfectant, chlorine, sickness and death. If I tried to see him I would get starched sheets and plastic chairs, the hours of waiting and not knowing, the wash of hospital visits the previous summer had seen. His shallow breathing and the ticking clock.

He had held on until winter but was gone with the last of the February frost.

Pounds, Shillings and Pence

By Clodagh Dunne

Dungarvan, Co. Waterford

As his daughter emigrates to seek work abroad, a father remembers the day he left home as a boy in hope of freedom and a better life.

My eyes were fixed on the railway tracks as I carried my daughter's bags to the platform. I breathed in deeply the crisp clean September morning air, refreshing my lungs and hoping that taking a strong breath would, in turn, help me to be strong, would help me to hold back my emotions as my wife and I bid our farewells to our daughter. Today she would emigrate.

Beams of sunshine penetrated a few weathered chinks in the platform's canopy and seemed to magically illuminate my daughter's presence. I watched as the light dashed through her shiny curls and they in turn, danced over and back with each nod of her head. She was in animated conversation with my wife, ensuring all the final checks were done. I watched too as my wife used her right index finger to tap in military sequence on each of the fingers of her left hand – checking and re-checking that everything was in place. Did my daughter have her mobile phone? Did my daughter have her money – or as I would often say to her – "Do you have your pounds, shillings and pence?" Did she have the address of who she was staying with? Did she have the details of our credit card if there was an emergency? Did she have a copy of her college degree, the computer memory stick which held her Curriculum Vitae? The list went on. I could see my daughter was merely satisfying my wife's constant questions by smiling and nodding her head. She knew it was her mother's way of distracting herself from the reality of the situation; avoiding, for as long as she could, the heartbreak of the imminent parting.

My daughter shot a smiling glance towards me and momentarily rolled her eyes upwards in a briefly shared amusement. An agitated impatience then started to overcome me as I looked down the long tracks yearning for, but simultaneously dreading, the train's arrival. I followed the tracks with my eyes for as far as I could until they eventually diminished and went out of sight, just before turning a corner underneath the rugged cliff face. My eyes scanned the magnificence of the rust-coloured rock and then a thousand memories came flooding back to me, of how, almost 50 years ago, I had gazed at that very same cliff through the tear-filled eyes of a 16 year old boy.

I remembered the hardness of my cumbersome suitcase as I sat on it on the damp platform, cold and tired. Never before or since had I felt so alone. I sat there remembering the tightness of my mother's embrace as she stood at the door that morning, clenching the corner of her apron and lifting it to her face as it sopped with the ocean of tears that flowed down her beautiful cheeks. The raucousness of the younger children did little to remove her despairing gaze from me. I recalled my younger brothers and sisters running in and out of the hallway, climbing onto my suitcase and then pulling it between them and fighting over it, some tugging on my jumper, and incessantly hanging from my mother's skirt crying out for her attention. But she stood there, as if impenetrable, unaware of the chaos surrounding her. I could feel the softness of her warm hands as she hurriedly pressed her fingertips and palms over every inch of my young face, studying my hair, my eyes, nose and mouth as if taking her very last look at me. She sobbed bitterly, tutting and biting her lower lip as she kissed me on my brow. I remembered too my own heartbreak and that rare feeling of being utterly alone with my mother, with no distractions, no time for anyone else, just me and me alone. I gallantly wiped away my own reluctant tears, placed my hands upon her shoulders and bravely and slowly moved myself away from her so that I could leave. And then I took a long deep breath, pushing my chest upwards and outwards, again somehow hoping that a strong breath would, in turn, help me to be strong.

Suddenly I thought I heard the sound of my daughter's train as I was startled back onto the platform beside her. She squinted her forehead in confusion as I said, "Twenty eight shillings, I think."

"What are you talking about, Dad? I was just asking you if you knew the cost of the train fare to Dublin. That's the only detail Sergeant Major Mam doesn't know and I'll have to pay when I get on," she explained.

"I told you we should have driven her to the airport; it would have been a far better plan and none of this awful waiting around," my wife interjected. But my daughter was adamant that she was having no teary goodbyes. The train station was as far as we were allowed to go.

My mind drifted again. Twenty eight shillings. Exactly what it cost me for my fare to Paddington Station, I remembered. Twenty eight shillings subtracted from the 5 pounds which I had borrowed from Mrs. Kennedy, the elderly wife of one of the neighbouring farmers.

I remembered the kindness and understanding in her face as I made my rehearsed promise to pay her back every penny as soon as I got settled in London. She knew my family well; she knew how hard my mother worked and how hard my father drank. She knew how all ten of us would sometimes have eaten porridge for our breakfast, for our dinner and for our tea and how we would have counted ourselves lucky to have had any food at all while doing so. She knew that none of us minded a hard day's work, how, from an early age, we would load the ass and cart with sticks and logs and sell them from door to door in the town four miles away. She did not doubt my honesty, my innocence, the conviction of my promise. And I remember sitting anxiously as she took the old red biscuit tin down from the top of the kitchen dresser and handed me the crisp five pound note. She patted the top of my head, told me everything would be all right, how everything would sort itself out, and she then walked over to the open fireplace where her purse was hidden away in a little old rusty tea caddy on the mantle. I could smell the charred and burnt woody stench, irrevocably caught up in every fibre of the purse's lining and I remember breathing it in as she handed me the small silver coin, saying,

"This is for yourself, love. This is not a loan." It was a shilling, 12 pence. For me, at that very moment, the shilling symbolised all that was good in the world, all that was kind and trusting. It gave me a confidence and a belief in myself that I would survive, that everything would be all right and I held it tightly in the palm of my hand as I said goodbye.

As I walked down the bohereen from Mrs. Kennedy's, I ran over my decision to leave again and again. I justified it to myself; it was not an easy choice. For the preceding months, I had been training as a deckhand on one of the fishing vessels anchored in the harbour of the little coastal village 12 miles away. I would awake at 4 am every morning and cycle the 12 long and dark miles to my job. I worked a hard, long day and at the end of every week I was handed 4 pounds and ten shillings. I cycled home and would hand up the entire amount to my father. I don't think he used this money for his drinking. At that time I can't remember him drinking all that much. As far as I knew, my earnings went into the household kitty and if you wanted anything for yourself, you had to ask for some money to be given back to you. It was this very detail which had sealed my fate and which was the reason I sat on the damp platform ready to emigrate as a boy of 16 and three months. I had asked my father for 6 pence out of my wages. I wanted to see a film in the cinema and that was the cost of a ticket in "The Gods". His refusal felt so unjust and so unfair that I decided I could take no more, that surely any existence, no matter how lonely, could be better somewhere else. I would make a new life for myself across the water. I wondered if my decision was the right one as I stared at the rust–coloured rock of the cliff face.

My daughter gripped me by the arm, "Dad, here it comes," she said as I caught sight of the shiny black train speeding down the tracks. Barely audible, it pulled into the station. My wife became increasingly flustered as the train came to a halt.

"Are you sure you have everything now? Phone? Money?" she began.

"Everything, Mam. I'll be fine. Stop. Stop," my daughter pleaded.

"It's all just so wrong," my wife sobbed as the tears flowed down her face. "We educated you. We did everything right. This was never supposed to happen again. I thought the days of emigration were long gone. It's all down to greed, those wretched property developers and their awful relentless greed. All this awful pain and heartache for money," she cried as she buried her head in my daughter's neck.

"Stop, Mam. I'll be fine. Times are much different now. I'll text you as soon as I get to Dublin," my daughter reassured both of us.

I placed her bag on the floor of the open carriage and turned and held her tightly as she said goodbye. The tears flowed down my cheeks as I studied every inch of her beautiful young face and I promised her that everything would be all right. She stepped onto the train and as she put out her hand to touch mine once more, I placed Mrs. Kennedy's silver shilling in her palm – in the hope that all that was good in the world would always be with her.

No Matter What

By Lucy Moore

Kilmore Quay, Co. Wexford

A job interview changes two people's lives.

I hear the back door slap open; Gracie stares over my shoulder with round curious eyes and refuses the spoonful of dinner I hold out.

"Kevin, the car won't start!"

I look at Deirdre and grin. I can't help myself – she looks fabulous, her corn coloured hair is drawn into a tight pony tail, the straight skirt of her suit and her high heels draw a wolf whistle from me. Even though we've been together for four years, sometimes I can't believe this bombshell is my wife.

Deirdre is unimpressed. "Cut it out, will you? You know how much we need this job. What will I do now?"

Gracie starts to whine. She holds her arms up to Deirdre and pushes herself up in the high chair.

"You're getting more dinner on her face than you're getting into her. Here, I'll do that," she takes the bowl and spoon from me, "you take a look at that car and see if you can get it going."

I hesitate by the door and watch for a moment. Deirdre coos Gracie into opening her mouth, where she deposits just the right amount for the child to manage. Gracie smiles and gurgles. I experience the old sense of being excluded.

"Yeah well, we were having fun," I mutter.

The sight of the Fiesta brings me back to reality. It was one of the economies we'd made when Deirdre decided not to go back to work after Gracie was born; we'd done a deal on her Audi for this and part payment for the hi-ab. I turn the key, fully expecting to find she's flooded it in her anxiety, but there isn't a gig out of it. I grip the wheel. Deirdre doesn't know how right she is - we do need her to get this job. The bank is threatening to bounce my cheques if I don't lodge money to reduce the

146

overdraft by Monday, but where am I going to get funds to do that? I've been to every customer that owes me money and they're all in the same boat as me.

I turn back to the house. The air is heavy with the scent of ripe apples and the ditch is laden with knots of sour-sweet blackberries; overhead blue-grey clouds roll in, promising rain. My head swims with worries. If Dee gets this job I could go into the bank and make a case for retaining our overdraft, but to do that she has to get to the interview. I kick at the vivid reds and yellows under my feet.

"You'll have to bring me," Deirdre says in her 'don't-argue-with-me' voice when I report back.

"All right, love, I'll change over the baby seat while you get Gracie ready. Have you seen the strap for the cab?"

"In the hall press."

I try not to take her shortness as criticism; she's uptight about the interview, I remind myself. Then I try not to think about how much she doesn't want to leave Gracie and go back to work. But it's only for three days a week and my mother and her mother said they'd help out. Anyway, she might not get the job and we've given Gracie a good start. I root around in the press. It's not as if Gracie has to go to a crèche every day from 8 till 6 and as soon as things pick up in the business Deirdre could-

"What are you doing?"

"Looking for the strap for the baby chair," I answer reasonably.

Her sigh cuts me.

"Here, you put Gracie's coat on, I'll find the strap." She sets about the same search, but more methodically.

"Come on, Princess, Mammy needs some peace to get her head right for her interview. Let's you and I get ready elsewhere."

I make gear changing noises and whisk her back into the kitchen. Gracie giggles and jabbers back at me and I forget about feeling peeved. Ten minutes later Deirdre walks in like a school girl who's forgotten her homework. Her face is flushed, a tendril of hair hangs down and her blouse pokes out over her skirt in places.

"What's wrong, love?" I ask.

"I can't find it," she says. "Gracie'll just have to go under the seatbelt with me."

I look at the clock. "I don't like that..." I falter.

"You think I do? What choice do we have? I have looked everywhere and there's no sign of it. I have to be there in half an hour and the journey will take twenty minutes in the truck. Kevin, jobs like this aren't advertised anymore, they are networked and only for Niamh McMahon remembering me, I wouldn't be getting this chance. Don't you know younger people are coming up all the time, with more IT skills than me? And things aren't exactly rosy here, I don't have money for a taxi - do you?"

That shot is unworthy of my Deirdre. I look at her, but say nothing. She is staring out the front window; her cheeks are still red and her eyes moist. The flower beds are changing from rivers of pink, red and purple to contours of leggy browns and greens. She's right, of course, this time next week I don't know if I'll even have money for groceries. I haven't told her the full extent of our problems, not wanting to burden her, but it appears that she knows.

"Let's go then," I hoist Gracie up onto my shoulders and head for the door in little jumps. When I reach Deirdre's side I stop.

"Now you, Little Missy, you just go an' purty yourself up again while I go tend to the horses. Yeehaw!"

She smiles and pushes me good naturedly towards the door and I breathe easy.

I have the engine running when she appears, looking elegant and cool; this time her hair is pinned into a smooth roll at the back of her head, but I can tell by the tightness of her mouth and the sound of her breathing that she is nervous.

"Tell me, Mrs. Kelly," I begin in a superior tone as soon as we reach the open road, "what do you see yourself bringing to this job, aside from great legs, that is?" I glance at where her skirt is pulled up and I can see a hint of thigh.

She giggles and playfully smacks my hand resting on the gear stick. Gracie tries to do the same but can't reach me. Deirdre adjusts her skirt as she thinks.

"What would I bring?" She hesitates only for a moment. "My commitment and my vision," and she's off. For the next ten minutes I listen to her observations about trends and markets, about how the recession necessitates changes in sound bites and ways in which advertising companies organise themselves.

How does she know all this? I wonder, she's been at home for over two years now, if her difficult pregnancy is taken into account. She's created a lovely home almost single-handedly because I work long hours; she is a super mother and yet it sounds like she's kept right up to date with every development in advertising.

I pull in at the end of the street and Deirdre squeezes out from under Gracie.

"We'll go to the park, give us a ring when you're finished. Knock 'em dead, Dee!" I wink at her, but she's busy smoothing down her skirt and patting her hair.

"Bye, loves." She waves. I watch every sinuous movement of her progress until she reaches the offices of Redmond, Corbally and Crosbie and disappears.

"Right, Princess, let's go have some fun." I lift Gracie down and set out for the park. My phone rings less than an hour later.

"Kev'? I'm out. Where are you?"

"We'll be there in two ticks. How did it go?"

"Good, I think," she giggles. "I can't wait to tell you. Hurry up."

"On our way."

She is leaning against the cab when we get there; she's let her hair down and it hangs like silk around her face. It smells like peaches - I used to tell her she should do those shampoo ads on the telly. But I haven't said anything like that to her for ages, I realise. She takes Gracie and pecks me on the cheek.

"Come on, let's go - I've loads to tell you." As I negotiate out into the traffic she begins. "You'll never guess what the first question he asked me was, 'Mrs. Kelly, what do you see yourself bringing to this firm?'"

"He did not!" We burst out laughing and Gracie joins in, squealing above us.

"He did. After that he asked what innovations I had in mind. I'd mentioned efficiencies around work-practices and other things."

"Like?" I prompt.

"Well, like working from home, for some of the time."

"Did he go for that?" I ask, taken by surprise.

"Kind of," she stops and draws in a deep breath. "Kev', he offered me a full-time job."

I glance at her, she's staring straight ahead.

"That's great, love," I reach across and pat her knee. "Well done." She smiles and we are silent. Full time? This is major - we'll have to take our time over this.

A black car with a single occupant races out of a side road on my right. Options swoop through my head. Hit the car? Swerve right and hit the tree? Swerve left into the path of an oncoming car? I pull left, then sharply right, trying to miss the approaching car. It might have worked if I'd had a full load, but as it is I am too high and light for the manoeuvre. We tip up onto two wheels and seem to hang there before slamming down onto the road. I feel a sharp pain in my hand, I struggle to turn to my family, but gravity holds me rigid. Close to my ear I hear metal splitting and screeching as the road claws greedily at the cab. Gracie shrieks, but there is no sound from Deirdre. Further away I can hear brakes squealing and people screaming. The truck eventually careens to a halt. Under the roars of the engine, under the screaming and shouting from outside I feel the weight of her silence press on my heart. I turn off the ignition. Then I hear her sobbing and a great whirlwind of relief blows through me.

"It's all right, love," I whisper.

"I thought you were dead," she cries, "there wasn't a sound out of you and look at your hand."

"My hand?" I can just see a bloody stump from the corner of my eye. I manoeuvre my head round to look at them, suspended under their seat belt. Two sets of round eyes stare down at me: Gracie, red faced and screaming; Deirdre, tear-filled and afraid. My family - once I get them out I am going to kill the idiot that caused this accident. I grin at Deirdre, she grins back.

"We need some help in here!" I call. "My wife and child are in here with me. Can you get them out?"

When I come round, Deirdre is by my bed.

"We're fine," she says before I have time to ask, "your mother has Gracie and there's not a mark on either of us."

She's still there when I open my eyes the next time; the low lighting announces it is night time. My hand hurts.

"Here," she hands me some pills and a tumbler of water, "for the pain," she explains. "Kev', I need to tell you something. Whatever happens from here we will be okay, do you know that?" I nod and try not to think of the pain in my missing fingers.

"Do you know how I know?" she asks, her voice sounds like a spoonful of thick honey. I struggle to pay attention. "Our baby could have been killed yesterday. The rear bars collapsed when we turned over, and went straight through where her seat should have been."

I nod again, my eyes fill with tears.

"I'm not finished yet, Kev'," she whispers. "You'll never guess what the first thing I saw was when I walked into the kitchen?"

"What?" I ask.

"The strap. Kev', the strap was on the work top." She takes hold of my good hand and squeezes it. "We're going to be fine, Kev', no matter what. We'll manage. Do you believe me?"

I look at her dear, confident face and smile.

"Sleep then, love. I'll still be here when you wake up."

MADONNA

A MEMORY BY PAT REID
Dublin

Donna, a young red-haired girl, leaves a lasting impression on one man's mind as he remembers her from his youth.

Barely a week passes by that I don't think of a girl I grew up with more than half a century ago. Her name was Madonna and she lived in the docklands area of Dublin. We kids just called her Donna. I was eight when we moved into the Cottages, next door to Donna, who was about my age. I first saw her as she lay sleeping on her window sill, her red-freckled face pressed against the cracked pane.

"Her name is Donna," my brother whispered. "She's simple."

The ancient Cottages had been built on reclaimed ground, and the sea must have resented the intrusion because it never stopped trying to get it back. The front walls bulged out, as if bloated from past floods. In summer, small flowers and weeds sprouted from these walls, filling the old grey house with vibrant colours.

Donna's mother, Kay, had a small wiry body and wore a frock that was held together with safety pins. Her home smelled of mothballs and oranges. Every evening in winter, Kay collected orange boxes from the stall sellers in Moore Street. These were used for firewood. The boxes lay stacked along the damp hallway. Our cottage wasn't as damp, but after a few years we moved around to the New Flats.

Kay wouldn't move. "I was born in Newfoundland and here I'll stay," she said. She was one of a very few who called this part of the city by its original name, Newfoundland Street.

Once Donna caught a pigeon and kept it in an orange box on her window sill. One day she held out a small folded body. "Why?" her eyes asked clearer than any words, "Why did it die?"

"I don't know, Donna," I said, "they just die."

Sometimes I passed by their home on Saturdays as Kay bathed Donna in front of the fire. As usual, the radio was on and Leo Maguire was urging listeners that "if you do sing, sing an Irish song."

First Kay used a fine comb, then she poured hot water into a tin bath and scrubbed Donna with Sunlight soap, singing a well-known song to which she always added her own words.

"There was a lovely, red-haired girl. Madonna was her name. She was born an' reared along the quays, in a place called Newfoundland. She was her mother's one true love, with eyes that shone like pearls. I'll hold her tightly in my arms, my lovely red-haired girl." Afterwards, Kay sat by the window holding Donna in her arms until her only child fell asleep.

Donna's father had worked as a crane driver on the docks. Shortly after Donna's birth he collected his wages one Friday, boarded the B and I boat to Liverpool and left forever. I never once heard Kay mention his name.

I got a job in a clothing factory when I was 13. On my way to Middle Abbey Street every morning, I'd see both of them leaning elbow-to-elbow on the window sill, watching the dockers walking down to work on the ships.

I can still recall the time that Kay suddenly died. At the graveside Donna looked lost and I wondered if she really knew what was happening. Shortly after the funeral Donna left the cottage, carrying her few belongings away. She took to sleeping in one of the empty old warehouse sheds on the quays. Sometimes my mother cooked a pot of white coddle and gave it to Donna on her way to mass on City Quay. Other local women, with barely enough to feed their own, would also save some food for Donna.

One day a Health Board official came by looking for Donna. When she left, Donna emerged from hiding, her long red hair covered in dirt and cobwebs. She waved at me and I waved back.

Donna began spending her time sitting on the quays, watching people who worked on the docks eating their lunch. When someone left food Donna would take it back to the shed to feed pigeons. Once again a Health Board official came looking for her, but Donna was gone. My mother went by the shed later with food. Donna wasn't there.

For weeks afterwards my mother kept looking across to the sheds, praying that she would see Donna moving about.

"God help her wherever she is," Mom would repeat, "she wouldn't survive in any of them homes."

When I recall that time, I hate to think of Donna alone and scared. My mother thought she might have gone to Liverpool, just like her father many years earlier. Somehow I doubted it. Yet I could not imagine her confined to any institution.

I can't forget my last sight of Donna; her sitting motionless outside the shed, legs stretched out, white face turned up to the wintry sun, her mouth open in a coughing spasm. As the sunlight shifted, Donna edged sideways to follow it. When it reached halfway across the concrete floor and began to slant away, she placed her feet on both sides of the patch of light. She gazed at it, unblinking, until it disappeared. Then she stood up, saw me and waved. I waved back. As she moved into her silent living space, a small, white pigeon followed her into the shadows.

ALSO KNOWN AS

By GERALDINE DU BERRY

Monaincha, Roscrea, Co. Tipperary

When Liam fled to London to make a new life for himself, he thought he left all his troubles behind in Ireland. How wrong he was!

" You're out of options," Miss Finn said, "I'm ringing her, Liam."

Liam flinched. He hadn't been called by that name since he'd left Ireland 30 years before. Thirty years ducking and diving, working on the lump and avoiding the Miss Finns of this world. With a sinking feeling though, he realised the social worker was right. The phone call would have to be made. For the first time in his life, Liam really was out of options.

An incident over a stolen bicycle had brought the police to his mother's door. Liam already had a cousin banged up in a reform school and from the rumblings he'd heard about that place, London seemed a much better option. With little hesitation and no explanation to his mother, Liam gathered a few belongings, slung his accordion over his back and fled.

On the boat over, the accordion proved itself invaluable. No doubt about it, music was a great ice breaker. After a few tunes, he struck up a conversation with an old boy from Galway who'd set him wise on how to survive in the big city, the best sites to find work, the best landladies to put him up. When they parted company in Euston Station, Liam threw his arms around the old boy and while thanking him profusely, removed his wallet full of cash and more importantly his social security card. And so, Liam McGrath left Ireland and arrived in London as Tom Ryan.

The years went by in a blur of hard work on the sites, hard drinking and music making in the evening. Liam lived one day at a time but then came the one day he had never reckoned on, the day of the fire. It had been relentless in its destruction. In under 30 minutes, the fire consumed everything in his life, everything except for the accordion. Liam had dashed back into the hall and grabbed his old companion from under the stairs. The firemen had roared at him in anger over such foolishness, but they didn't realise that the accordion had livened up many a lonely evening, opened doors in pubs and made him a few bob when times were tough.

You saved my life a few times, Liam thought, his hand resting on the accordion, the least I could do was return the compliment.

But now, homeless, penniless and reduced to only the clothes he stood up in, the fire had forced Liam into Miss Finn's office and her relentless questions. The social worker sighed inwardly as she regarded the man seated in front of her. The broken veins across his face spoke to her of years of hard drinking but the calloused hands spoke of years of hard work.

"Liam," she said softly, "without some means of identification, I cannot process your claim, we need your birth certificate. We need to ring your family in Ireland."

Liam put his head in his hands and felt ashamed. His face burned as he looked at Miss Finn. This is not a person who would have treated her family as shabbily as he had. "Feckless" is what his father had called him. Liam hadn't known what that meant at the time but he understood now. The years of broken promises to his mother flooded his mind. The assurances of a few bob soon, of a holiday next year, of a letter more often all came back. He hadn't even made it to her funeral. He thought of his sister, Sheila, only 15 when he left, she'd had a mop of blond curls on what their mother called "an old head on young shoulders." She'd be 45 now. A lifetime had passed. Miss Finn's hand hovered over the phone.

"Stop," he said, "I'll do it. I have to explain myself."

Sheila McGrath came home tired and irritable. Things were starting to become unmanageable. She flopped into the chair and thought over her day.

Something's got to give, she thought. I can't keep it up. The choice before her was stark: give up her job, sell her house and move in to care for her ailing father or put Dad into a home. Tears pricked Sheila's eyes.

The light blinking on the answering machine caught her eye. There were two messages. Wearily, Sheila pressed play. The first message was a dud, some garbled conversation in the background and a fumbled hang up.

Either a wrong number or some idiot not used to answering machines, thought Sheila. She sat bolt upright as the second message played out, a social worker calling from England and something to do with Liam and a fire.

Sheila couldn't take it in. She hadn't given much thought to Liam in recent years. She hadn't seen him since she was 15 for heaven's sake! She struggled to remember their youth together. A memory came vividly to her of Liam sitting in the kitchen playing the accordion. Dad would give a rare smile as he looked at Liam and say, "he sure can make that thing talk." Over the years he had been reduced to a couple of dog eared photographs her mother had kept in her room. "An auld rogue" her father would say of him. Her mother, however, had never stopped looking out for the letters that came only sporadically from London. Sheila remembered the resentment she felt each time Liam deigned to contact their mother. Mam's obvious delight and relief at hearing from him had confused Sheila. How could Mam read and re-read those ridiculous letters full of false promises and if, as the letters said, he was doing so well in London, why didn't he ever send Mam a few quid? Why hadn't he come to see her? When Liam hadn't shown up for Mam's funeral, Dad never mentioned his name again. Sheila found out later that Dad had wired Liam the fare and he still hadn't shown. Like all of Liam's post from home, the money had been sent "care of Tom Ryan".

"Who the hell is Tom Ryan?" Dad would ask. Mam presumed he must be Liam's roommate or one of the lads from work.

Strange, Sheila thought, but then strange just about summed up Liam.

Miss Finn drummed her pencil on her desk. She wondered if the McGraths would return her call. Liam had been fixed up in temporary lodgings with Mrs. Saunders and been given enough money to tide him over. Miss Finn knew these arrangements couldn't last long, without Liam's birth certificate neither the insurance policy nor the state benefits claim could go any further. Miss Finn sighed. She'd done a little digging about Liam and found very little. Unknown to the police was the only positive she could find, but then, he seemed unknown just about everywhere she looked. Her usual sources had drawn a blank when it came to Liam McGrath.

Liam sat in his room in Mrs. Saunders boarding house and he too wondered if Miss Finn would hear from home. "What the hell is keeping them? It's been a week since the call. It's all very well for Sheila, cocked up back there being pandered to by the old man, spoiling her rotten over the years, while I've been here working in all weathers trying to make a living," he grumbled. In his heart of hearts though, Liam knew that Sheila owed him nothing. This predicament was of his own making, but even so, Liam couldn't help feeling agitated and annoyed at the lack of response from Ireland. Resentment welled up in him. He went for a pint.

The call finally came. Miss Finn was relieved to hear Sheila McGrath identify herself and the social worker gave her the details of Liam's circumstances.

"Give me his address," Sheila said, "and I'll make sure he gets his birth certificate." Sheila hung up, smiled grimly and said to herself, "He'll definitely get it because I'm going to hand deliver it."

As Liam pushed open the door of the George Pub, he was greeted by Har' and Alan.

"Tom Ryan! Where've you been? We heard about the fire. Sit up there and have a pint. Tell us all about it."

As Liam levered himself up on the barstool, Sheila was getting out of a cab at the address given to her by Miss Finn. She straightened her skirt, took a deep breath and knocked on Mrs. Saunders' door.

"Hello, eh, Mrs. Saunders?"

"Yes," said the lady of the house, while eyeing Sheila circumspectly.

"I'm Sheila McGrath, here to see my brother, Liam."

"Liam McGrath, you say?" said Mrs. Saunders.

"Yes, Liam McGrath."

"I'm sorry, dear," said Mrs. Saunders, "but there's nobody here by that name."

Mrs. Saunders had been a landlady a long, long time and prided herself on being a good judge of character. Over the years she'd had many ladies call to her door looking to speak to her gentleman lodgers. She'd seen the frightened types with obvious bumps under their dresses, official types with briefcases under their arms and dodgy ones with dark shadows under their eyes. Mrs. Saunders' instinct had never let her down, she always knew who to admit and who to refuse.

"Come in, dear," she said, "there seems to be some confusion. Let's have a cup of tea and a chat."

Sheila followed Mrs. Saunders in and as the two sat down, she noticed an old accordion that had seen better days lying in the corner of the room.

"Do you play, Mrs. Saunders?" Sheila asked, indicating the accordion.

"Dear me, no," replied the landlady, "that belongs to Tom Ryan, one of my lodgers. It's not in great shape; it was damaged in a fire."

"Where is he? Where's Tom?" asked Sheila, her heart racing.

"He's gone to the George Pub on the corner."

Adrenalin coursed through Sheila's veins as she scooped up the accordion and promising Mrs. Saunders to return with both Tom and the accordion, she headed for the George.

With a shaking hand, Sheila pushed open the door of the pub and walked in. Unsure of herself now, she glanced around uncertainly and spotted a group of men seated around a table. One of the men was seated with his back to her, but Sheila started as she spotted the blond hair so like her own.

"Ah, Tom," one of the men was saying, "can't believe you didn't bring the squeeze box. A few tunes is just what we need."

Sheila approached the table and put the accordion down on it, saying, "Go on, Liam, Dad always said you could make that thing talk."

Liam looked up in alarm. His first instinct was to feign ignorance, tell this woman she had the wrong man and laugh it off as a case of mistaken identity. The lads looked at him, waiting. Sheila looked at him, waiting.

"Lads," he said, "this is my sister, Sheila. Now you'll have to excuse us, she's come a long way and it's been a long time." Before any questions could be asked, Liam took Sheila by the elbow and gently but firmly steered her out the door.

Once out on the street, sister and brother regarded one another and unsure of what to say or do next, it was left to Sheila to make the first move.

"Well here we are, Liam, or should I say Tom?" she laughed awkwardly. Liam rubbed his forehead, covering his eyes and struggled desperately to gather his thoughts. Sheila felt a rush of pity for the confused, bedraggled man beside her.

"Come on, Liam, let's go back to Mrs. Saunders' place and talk."

Mrs. Saunders saw them coming and knew here were two in need of some privacy. "Go on into the good room," she said, "fire's on and there's plenty of tea and sandwiches waiting for you." Liam and Sheila sat down, the talking began and went on until night fell and the fire had long gone out. As Sheila took his room for the night, Liam lay down on the couch and for the first time in 30 years, he didn't feel alone.

The sound of the telephone ringing woke him next morning.

"It's Miss Finn on the line for you," came the voice of Mrs. Saunders through the door. Liam took the phone and the story of Sheila's arrival, of her having the birth certificate came tumbling out.

"Liam," Miss Finn interrupted him, "I'm afraid there's bad news. I've a message from Ireland. Your father passed away during the night."

Seeing Sheila at the foot of the stairs, Liam handed the phone to her and went up to his room, his head reeling. "What will I do, Sheila?" he asked his sister.

"The right thing, Liam, for once in your bloody life! Do the right thing," Sheila snapped.

"I'll get packing," he said. The three women sprang into action. Mrs. Saunders produced a reasonable suit and black tie left behind by a long departed lodger. Miss Finn assured them she would sort out Liam's affairs now that the paperwork was complete and Sheila booked their passage back to Ireland.

Liam was silent for virtually the whole journey. He sensed Sheila's irritation with him. They couldn't fly, he had no passport. She had to do all the driving, he had no licence. She did all the crying for their dead father, he had no tears.

Panic mounted in Liam's chest as the boat docked in Dun Laoghaire.

What possessed me? he thought. His mouth ran dry at the thoughts of long forgotten relatives waiting at home. What would they say? What could he say?

Sheila broke into his thoughts, "Look, we'll stay in a hotel here tonight and drive on home in the morning. We'll both be in a better frame of mind then."

Sheila slept fitfully. She, too, was anxious about Liam's return and the reaction he would get. She was also hurt and confused that Liam had shown little or no sadness about Dad's death. Sheila couldn't bear to think about Dad right now, it was all so overwhelming. As dawn broke, Sheila dragged herself from the bed and as she was making her way to the bathroom, she saw it. A note had been pushed under her door during the night. It read:

Sheila, sorry, but I've gone back to London. Can't go home right now but hope to see you in the summer and will send a few bob soon.

Liam

Party Games

A MEMORY BY MARGARET DWANE
Johnstown, Co. Kildare

Two sisters learn that it doesn't pay to tell lies.

When my sister and I were young teenagers in the 1940s, times were lean. We had one lady's bicycle to share between my mother, my sister and I. My sister and I were allowed to use it to visit friends and to travel to local parties. We had to decide between ourselves how we would share its use.

One Sunday during our summer holidays from boarding school, we were invited to a big birthday party in a small town around four miles from our home. We told our parents it was at a friend's house not too far away and asked if we could borrow the bike so that neither of us would have to walk too far. My mother said fine but that we needed to be home by 11.

We left at 7.30 pm. My sister had decided that she would ask the priest's housekeeper whom she was friendly with, for a loan of her bicycle for a few hours. She had lent it on a number of occasions and she had no difficulty lending it this time either. When we got to town we put our bikes into the bicycle park. Mr. Judge looked after the bikes parked there for parties and dances. It cost sixpence (a tanner) per bike. He put a sticker with a number on the back mudguard; it had his name and address on it. He gave us a corresponding ticket to show him when we returned to collect our bikes. We had a wonderful night singing and dancing, ate a lovely supper and consumed lots of lemonade. The night ended so quickly.

We got lots of offers to be escorted home but unfortunately, we could not accept any as we had to leave early to get home on time. It was a rush but we made it and managed to return the bicycle to the priest's housekeeper. I put our bike back in the shed as usual, and we scurried inside skitting and laughing at all the antics of the night. We told our parents a pack of white lies about the party and headed to bed.

We spent the next day laughing and joking and regretting that we couldn't have taken up some of the offers we got to be escorted home.

My mother arrived home at about 3.30 that afternoon. She finished her dinner and then asked my sister and I to go to the parlour and tell her tales of the night before. I let my sister do the talking as she was quicker with lies than I was.

"So you shared the bicycle between you last night?" my mother asked. I knew straight away that she knew we had lied but my sister didn't. I eyeballed her and tried to signal her to stop talking but she just kept waffling on, burying us deeper. From her bag my mother pulled out one of Mr. Judge's stickers.

"I wonder how this got on the mudguard of our bike? Can either of you enlighten me?"

My sister nearly fainted with fright, while I couldn't keep a straight face and I started to laugh uncontrollably.

"You're a pair of Hectors," my mother said, "I will not worry your father with tales of your lies, but ye will not be out of this house for the next month." For the rest of the summer my mother did not take her eyes off us.

A week later I stole out of the house and headed up to the local barracks and borrowed a bike from the local guard. It was just up at the top of the hill from our house. He often lent me his bike on the quiet. I told him I wouldn't be long and not to tell anyone.

"If your father ever finds out, I know nothing about it," he said nervously.

Most people were afraid of my father; he was huge and had a short fuse.

"Don't worry," I said, "he'll know nothing about it."

I turned my coat inside out and pulled an old straw hat down over my hair and headed off to the fair. I had to pass our house and was fairly certain I wouldn't be recognised with my jacket inside out. I nearly fell off the bike when I saw my father heading out the back door with a bucket on his arm. He was about to go milking. I peddled faster down the hill and sang my heart out. I spent an hour at the fair and then headed back to the barracks and returned the bike. I tidied myself up and headed down the hill and in to the back kitchen, happy that I had succeeded with my latest escapade.

"Where have you been, my fine young maid?" my father whispered in my ear.

"Just up at the barracks," I replied.

"Glad you didn't stay long," Dad said. "You know, Margaret, while I was heading out to the milking parlour, some lunatic headed past cycling madly and screeching at the top of his voice. I was tempted to go and report it to the guard but then I noticed it was his bike they were on. What do you think about that, my girl?

LAURA'S DAY

By DEIRDRE LANZILLOTTI

Clonsilla, Dublin

Instead of being caught up with house chores and other mundane day-to-day stuff, Laura decides to take a break for one day and enjoy life

T he morning had eased itself gently into the early afternoon and Laura still sat reading on an old, comfortable sofa. She had refilled her coffee cup two or three times. As each chapter ended, Laura jumped up to complete one or two tasks around the house. Clothes were washing in the utility room, the comforting smell of a stew gently bubbling in the oven, filled the house. The post had been checked as Laura had heard it arriving on the hall floor. Beginning each new chapter of her book, Laura felt a comfort embrace her; the same comforting feeling she had after an evening bath when she had slipped into her cotton pyjamas and slippers. The characters in the story had become so familiar that Laura found herself almost missing them as she spoke briefly to a friend who called on the phone to make an appointment for coffee. Last night Laura had decided that today was going to be "Laura's Day". She had kissed her only child goodbye that morning as she had left for university, happily knowing that today she would spoil herself by doing a few of her favourite things.

The coldness of the early morning had been replaced by a soft autumn sunshine and the light of the sun as it shone through the window reminded her that she would have to make a start if she were going to complete all of the things she had promised her diary she would do on the previous evening. Well, number one was completed. She had snuggled lovingly over her book while sipping on coffee. Laura rose from the sofa and stretched her arms. A smile was visible on her face. Still thinking about the mad escapades of the beautiful heroine in the gothic novel she had been reading, she was able to forget for a few moments that only a few weeks before she had lost her job. She had been called into the office where she had worked for more than 15 years, to learn that the company was downsizing and her position was gone.

Laura went into the kitchen and turned off the cooker. She quickly hung the clothes that had finished spinning in the washing machine, on the clothes horse in the kitchen. The day had an air of uncertainty about it. She was afraid that it might rain. Laura went upstairs and washed her hands with a sweet smelling soap. She left her book on the bedside locker. She brushed her hair, applied some make up and sprayed herself with a perfume her daughter had bought her for her birthday. There was a lightness in her heart as she sat into her car and drove to Phoenix Park. Here she parked the car and walked downtown. She walked towards Smithfield. Firstly she was going to find a coffee shop and order a large latte with a meringue dripping with fresh cream and fruit. With this done, she walked down the quays alongside the Liffey. The familiar buildings and streets kept her company. Like a sponge she allowed herself absorb all the smells and sounds of the city she had first come to love while waiting in a queue for fish and chips on O'Connell Street as a child with her mother.

Today Laura just wanted to walk and walk. Today she would walk as far as the Peppercanister Church. She wanted to walk down streets and laneways that were familiar to her. The sounds of her own house had become a little stifling to her in the last few weeks; her daughter was gone for most of the day. She just wanted to hear the lilting sounds of the local voices as they went about their daily business. Laura observed as people rushed across streets, dodging the traffic. There were young people giggling and chatting on roadside kerbs. The names of pubs she would have had a drink in as a young woman passed her by; the street corner where she had often waited anxiously for the man who would later become her husband. He had died ten years earlier. Laura didn't feel sad, only a sense of calmness as she felt the intimacy of the city enfold her.

Laura entered a bookshop on Dawson Street and browsed for a while in the literature section where the gothic novels hid, before choosing a book which she knew would keep her good company as the dark winter evenings approached. She wandered a while through the floors of the shop. Her eyes glimpsed the travel books and she allowed herself be drawn towards them. She couldn't help but be fascinated by the colourful pictures of exotic temples and ornate cathedrals on the book covers. Such beautiful places. She heard the drip drop of rain as it gently fell upon the pavement outside. She knew it would just be a short shower but she was glad that she hadn't left clothes hanging outside in the garden to dry. She placed the travel book back on the shelf. That would be an adventure for another day. Today Dublin was her host and as she reached inside her handbag for her umbrella and walked towards the exit of the shop, she was greeted by a crisp coldness in the air which made her put up her hood and zip her jacket fully.

Laura walked towards St. Stephen's Green and stepped inside the park. It was a little too cold for people to sit down for too long as they did in the summer. An old man with a faded cap was selling prints near the pond where she had played as a child. He nodded towards her. Laura nodded sadly back, knowing that she was not going to buy anything from him. She hurried towards the exit. She walked more quickly now down along Baggot Street. It would be another ten minutes or so before she reached the church and the evening was already closing in. The sound of the phone in her bag made her jump for a moment. It was a text message from her daughter saying that she would be a bit late home but that she was looking forward to having dinner together. She finished the message with a big smiley face which made Laura laugh. Laura knew that she had probably spent too long that morning reading her book and that it would be almost dark by the time she reached the church. Her step quickened and shortly after she reached the door to the building, she didn't want to go inside. She had just wanted to see if the Georgian church was as splendid as she had remembered as a child in the company of her mother. Touching the door of the church with her hand, she turned away and made for home.

The drizzle had stopped but Laura still nestled in the cosiness of the hood of her jacket. Her ears were warm and she felt content. Laura had promised her diary that she would stop off at a bakery and buy an apple pie for dessert. It was her daughter's favourite. Having done this, she walked back towards the quays. The rain was starting again; a little heavier this time. A bus which would bring her back to Phoenix Park was approaching its stop. Laura ran, boarded the bus and paid the fare. She sat at the back of the bus where a few elderly ladies with blue tinted perms and with shopping trolleys, which took up most of the aisle, were complaining endlessly about the weather. Laura reached her stop, thanked the driver and ran the remaining length of the journey back to her car. She opened the door and almost sank into the seat with the fatigue in her legs. She sat for a few minutes before starting the engine. Putting on the windscreen wipers and the heat in the car, she started the journey towards home. The traffic didn't bother her. She was looking forward to seeing her daughter. The rain was easing as Laura arrived home and opening the door she could still smell the welcoming odour of stew which she had left in the oven. She switched the oven on at a very low heat. The food would be tender and ready to be served up when her daughter came home. She then turned on the heat to warm up the house. She wrapped a bottle of red wine in a tea towel and placed it on the radiator to let it warm through. Opening the bottle, she settled down to watch an episode from a DVD boxset she had treated herself to, while still working and which she had promised her diary she would watch.

The room felt cosy, not stifling as it had of late. Laura couldn't see the speckled dots of damp which had formed along the edges of the blinds or the peeling wallpaper over the radiator where she often left clothes to dry. It was her home and she felt happy. The photographs of her husband, parents and daughter on the mantelpiece seemed to smile out at her as she nestled on the couch. Laura watched the DVD, absorbed in the medical drama unfolding. When it was finished she laid the table for the dinner. Her daughter arrived shortly later. Laden down with a heavy bag of books which she threw in a corner, she kissed her mother while all the time talking about things that had happened to her during the day. Laura listened attentively. They sat down to dinner, each enjoying the other's company. Laura was happy to witness the eagerness with which her daughter ate the stew and they both lingered over the deliciousness of the apple pie. Laura revealed little about her day. It was to remain a secret between herself and her diary. Mother and daughter cleared away the dishes and tidied up the kitchen. Offering her daughter a glass of wine, they sat down to watch the news. Her daughter then left to go upstairs as she had work to complete for college. Laura wished her goodnight.

Upstairs Laura ran herself a bath with so many bubbles that the bubbles toppled over the side of the bath onto the floor. Laura soaked her tired muscles in the warm water and reflected on the happiness the day had brought her. Memories of a vanishing youth had been recaptured. Happy days spent with her mother had been relived in her mind as she had walked so deliberately through the same streets they had walked together hand in hand. She felt her thoughts drift happily to similar days she had spent with her own daughter. Stepping out from the bath she dried herself with a large, soft towel. Blowing her hair dry at the mirror, she felt she still looked youthful. Her eyes were bright. Her hair was soft and curled gently at the ends. Her daughter still told her how lovely she looked and this only made her love her daughter more. She certainly didn't feel so worried today that she had no job to go to in the morning.

When dry, she dressed herself in her pyjamas and slippers, locked the house up for the night and went to bed. Propped up on three or four pillows she reached for her book which was beckoning to her from the bedside locker. Laura prepared herself for the next exhilarating adventure that would befall her heroine. As she reached the end of the chapter sheer tiredness forced her eyes to close. Laura switched off the light. She heard with comfort movement from the room next door as her daughter changed position in the bed. Laura pulled the blankets close to her chin. She let out a soft sigh and smiled. Today had been a wonderful day; certainly a day to record in her diary. Tomorrow would be an equally lovely day. Why? Hadn't she made an appointment to meet her best friend for coffee! Laura could already smell the rich aroma of freshly brewed coffee and taste the large fruit scone dripping with melting butter. Laura drifted happily off to sleep.

THE HEARSE

A MEMORY BY NORA BRENNAN
Kilkenny City, Co. Kilkenny

A woman remembers a funeral from her childhood.

When news hit the parish that Jack Murphy was dead, a gloom set into our house. My mother spoke little, a sure sign that the dark cloak of mourning had descended and would shroud our household for the following few days. She never left the corner by the fire. Instead, she sent my sister and me to Jack Murphy's wake. We were ten and 11 years of age.

"Sorry for your troubles," we said, shaking hands with family members. We were led upstairs into a small room where chairs lined the walls and a large bed filled the centre. I had never seen a dead body before and was frightened, staying close to my sister and near the door. The lace curtains were blowing in the breeze. The man could have risen already for all I knew and was back on a visit. I glanced at the bed. Just above the wrought iron bed frame were white knobbly fingers clasped together and entwined with a rosary beads.

I knew from my mother that we should stay in the room long enough to say our prayers: one Our Father, the Apostles' Creed, one decade of the Rosary and the Glory Be. Me and my sister and a corpse for company. I fixed my eyes on the altar table beside the bed, moving from candle flames to candle sticks and avoiding the black wooden crucifix that stood in the middle, Jesus strung out as I had seen him several times before. There was a small glass bowl of holy water to the front and a sprig of box shrub for the priest to use. My sister thought otherwise. She took the bushy shrub and showered the man with holy water, shaking it out good and strong the way she saw the priest do it when he blessed the congregation. After another handshake with family members downstairs, we hurried home to tell my mother who we met and what we had seen.

"They offered us tea too but you said not to take it," my sister said.

"You're good girls," came the feeble response.

The next day I kept watch from an upstairs window. In the afternoon, I saw the hearse go up the road, a wooden box visible in the long window. I hurried downstairs to report what I had seen. My mother was staring into the ashes. Whatever it was that caused her sorrow, it oozed out of her like dampness through the walls in winter. An hour later I was back at the window to see the final cortège go down the narrow road.

"There were twelve cars after the hearse," I said, hoping my breezy comment would shift the gloomy air.

In the parish all cars were used when there was a funeral. They carried family and friends who had no other transport. It was the biggest funeral a parish ever saw if the ditches near the church were lined with Volkswagen Beetles, Ford Angleas and Morris Minors. My father always brought back details.

"A big crowd, people couldn't fit inside the church door. I saw George there and Pakie. No sign of Keeffes. They mustn't have patched up their differences." And so it went.

When he finished his account of removals and burials, my mother's question was always the same: "What way was she dressed?"

"They were all in black. She had a black cap and coat." Even the mention of the word black added more darkness to the room.

Each time a loss occurred in our parish, my mother sat by the fire with a glazed look I grew familiar with in the years that followed. It wasn't until I reached adulthood and read the names of her loved ones on the family grave, that I realised the extent of her sorrow. And discovered too that she did not attend any of their funerals. I'm not sure why. Perhaps others thought they were protecting her at the time or it was considered men's work to shoulder the weight of funerals. Whatever the circumstances, I felt that whenever she heard of a death in the years that followed, she disappeared to a place in herself where only the ghosts of her loved ones could keep her company. I imagine they coaxed her to let go of the darkness, encouraged her to step out and be a part of the community joined in prayers, singing the soul of Jack Murphy back into the heavens.

She Wasn't the Worst

By Joan Biggar
Ardrossan, Scotland

A lonely district nurse sees her Prince Charming and makes an attempt to be with him but will she be successful?

Everybody in the village liked Nurse O'Hare. Well, you couldn't help liking the soul, she was so cheery, and had such a hearty laugh; a ray of sunshine much admired and respected. To show their gratitude for her care, people insisted on giving her wee mindings of toiletries, boxes of chocolates etc. At Christmas, she received cards by the score.

However, although it was agreed that she wasn't the worst, no man came courting her. There wasn't much social life in the village - the young folk went clubbing in the nearest town, but the more mature residents had to be content with the occasional whist drives and dances in the village hall. When Nurse O'Hare had time to attend these she rarely lacked for dancing partners. There were always former patients or their relatives to invite her up onto the floor.

"I'll need to give the nurse a dance," Men with geriatric mothers would tell their drinking cronies, who would nod in agreement. "She's been very good to mammy, so she has."

Or a local lady killer's wife, exhausted by the Latin American Medley would order her more energetic husband to "Away and dance with the nurse now. And ask her about Declan's tonsils while you're at it," when she saw her man eyeing up a flighty piece.

Dancing with Nurse O'Hare was no hardship. She moved as confidently on the dance floor as she did in her clinic, and laughed uproariously at a man's weakest jokes. Most were glad to ask her up to dance. However, she secretly envied the women who came with their own partners and stayed with them all evening. Sitting on the sidelines with a bright smile on her face, even when nobody had approached her to say, "good evening, nurse", she watched those couples, admiring how their steps matched so perfectly, their bodies moving as one. How, when they returned to their seats at the end of a dance, the man's arm would fall gently round the woman's shoulders and their heads would incline together whilst they talked, their breath mingling.

That was the way Nurse O'Hare longed to be with her dream man, who was by no means a figment of her imagination, or some television star. He was, in fact, a local farmer called Hugh Fitzpatrick. He was tall and lean, and rather aristocratic looking in a rugged way, she thought. Although approaching 40, he was a bachelor still and rarely attended village functions but when he did, most of his time was spent having a craic with his cronies. He had never asked her for a dance and she had no hopes that he ever would as he had nothing to thank her for, unlike the men with ailing elderly parents or pregnant wives.

Thinking of him as she sat in the chintzy lounge of the snug little nurse's home, which she had all to herself now as the other district nurse was married and had moved in with her husband, Nurse O'Hare sighed gustily and stirred restlessly in her armchair. Leisure time could be a drag when she had nobody with whom to spend it with.

Languor left her when the telephone shrilled out an urgent summons.

"District Nurse," she told the caller brightly. "How can I help you?"

"I was wondering if you could do me a wee favour?" asked a slow, deep voice. "I was showing a new lad I've taken on how to pulverise turnips, and some grit got in my eye, which is a bit of a nuisance, but it seems a trivial thing to take to the on-call doctor. Can you help, d'you think? I don't like to impose."

"No problem!" Nurse O'Hare assured him promptly. He was a farmer by the sound of things. Could it possibly be...? "Come down to the clinic," she invited. "You know where it is? I'm off duty actually, but the Nurse's residence is right next door. And your name is?"

"Hugh Fitzpatrick," her welcome caller told her. "Yes, I know where you are. I was at the clinic for my anti-tetanus jabs. I'll be with you in ten minutes."

"Make it twenty," Nurse O'Hare told him. She had a lot to do prior to his visit and didn't want to risk looking hot and bothered. Freshen up, spray on some light cologne, apply a discreet make-up, do her hair. Oh dear. This golden opportunity to become better acquainted with her dream man would come on a bad hair day, when her naturally curling topknot was at its most unruly. Then there was a tray to set ready with the best china and a plate of chocolate biscuits, he might be tempted to stay for a cuppa, and the television papers to check. Luck seemed to be with her as far as the telly was concerned. There was a farming documentary due to start soon, followed by a mystery play. If he was at a loose end, well, wouldn't it be great to have a cosy evening with him? Just an hour or two. That wasn't asking much surely, she prayed.

Rain was falling softly when Hugh Fitzpatrick parked his sleek Jaguar discreetly in a side street near the clinic-cum-nurse's residence. Drops of water sparkled on his crown of dark red hair as Nurse O'Hare ushered him into the room at the clinic where she attended to minor procedures. She found the grit lodged under his eyelid and expertly removed it, completing the treatment by splashing a few drops of lotion into both of his beautiful grey eyes, one of which was slightly bloodshot still. He looked up at her trustingly from his seat on the plastic chair of the clinic treatment room and his nostrils quivered slightly as the scent of jasmine wafted from the pulse points of his ministering angel, to mingle with the sensible smell of antiseptic.

"That's grand. Just grand," he assured her, as she stood smiling down at him. "I'm much obliged to you, nurse."

"Well, let's see if you can find your way into the sitting room," she suggested, opening the door, which led from the clinic to the nurse's living quarters and ushering him through.

The sitting room was cosy, the fire burning brightly, the miniature brass ornaments on the mantelpiece sparkling and the chairs in their frilly, flowery skirts holding out welcoming arms.

"My, you've got a really nice place here," Hugh Fitzpatrick remarked approvingly. "Do you have it all to yourself?" He stood solidly in the middle of the carpet like an oak tree that had sprung up from the Axminster flowerbed, with no thought of how the spider had captured the fly through an invitation into the parlour.

"Oh yes," she said. "I've got nobody to fall out with," and her laugh rang out again as she skilfully directed him to the largest and most comfortable easy chair. He sank down into the plush seat, reflecting that, like bagpipes, Nurse O'Hare's laugh sounded best out in the open air rather than in confined spaces. He smothered the unkind thought.

"What's on the box tonight, I wonder?" she mused casually as she pressed the remote control of the television. "Well, would you believe it! A farming documentary! Try your eye on that."

How long did she expect him to stay? Before he had time to think how he could get away. She was asking if he would like a drink, which prompted him to unfold his lean body and stand up, shaking his head and holding up a hand in refusal as though to fend her off.

"No, no, not for me," he said. "I've taken up enough of your time as it is. And there is someone waiting for me in the motor."

Well aware that he would seem ignorant in leaving so abruptly, he looked round in hope of seeing a collection box for some charity or other into which he could put a generous donation, but there was none. All he spotted in his scan of the room was a tray set for tea on a corner table and an almost empty chocolate box on the bureau. Would it be in order just to give the nurse money? Oh no, no! She might think he was offering her a tip and be offended.

"You should have brought your friend in," she was saying now.

"Och, sure it wasn't worth it for such a short time," he said. "She knows I'm in safe hands here. I appreciate your bothering to see me, but I'll get away now and leave you to a pleasant evening."

"What do you mean?" Nurse O'Hare asked sharply to his surprise. He nodded in the direction of the dainty tray, spread with a cloth she had embroidered on lonely evenings and harebell patterned china.

"Oh that!" she said and shrugged. "No, I don't expect anyone to visit. I may be called out, in fact."

"You have a busy time of it," he said, edging towards the door. "But it's nice to be wanted. I'll say goodnight then and thank you again."

He held out his hand for her to shake and as his fingers closed round her much smaller hand, it quivered like a captured bird. This surprised him and made him look at Nurse O'Hare properly for the first time that evening. Until then his mind had been preoccupied with Kay, who was hell bent on seeing some sci-fi film which hadn't come out on DVD yet. Why did he always give way to the wishes of demanding wee besoms like her, young enough to be his daughters, who saw him as a challenge because he was still a bachelor at his age?

It was a woman such as the nurse he should be taking up with and not before time. She was beautiful in her way, rounded and rosy, reminding him of a ripe apple and with big brown eyes. Their colour matched that of her hair now escaping in little tendrils from the way she had styled it. He wished he was spending the evening with her in this cosy room after his hard day's work, drinking tea, eating hot buttered toast and watching TV. Together, side by side on the sofa.

"You're a grand girl," he told her sincerely, but she took her hand, which he had been squeezing from his and turned away. It would take more than a compliment to console her for his early departure. She briskly preceded him into the hall and opened the front door.

"My regards to your young lady, whoever she is." She would not bring herself to ask. Ask the name of the girl he was evidently so eager to be with. However, he felt somehow obliged to explain his situation.

"She's Kay Miller," he said. "Oh she's far too young for me, you don't need to tell me and spoilt, too. It's really her father I'm friendly with..."

"None of my business," she told him. "Enjoy yourselves."

She laughed again and this time there was a note of derision in her laughter. He winced, thinking it implied that he was weak willed, but it was at herself. Oh, what a fool she had been! The name of Kay Miller had fallen on her heart like a clod on a coffin. Men like Hugh Fitzpatrick, apparently confirmed bachelors, represented a challenge to twenty somethings like Kay Miller, her of the blue eyes, jet black hair and snow white skin like the heroin of a Celtic fairytale. He had got his eye fixed so he could take her to a sci-fi film.

She closed the door resisting an impulse to slam it, went back in to the sitting room and slumped down in the chair he had vacated. Already the chintz was cool. Impatiently she switched off the television. Outside darkness was falling fast, and the night crept into the room where she sat in silence, lacking the will to move, even to the kitchen where the kettle she had filled with hope in her heart, waited to be switched on. In the dying light, she reached for the chocolate box on the bureau and ate the few it still contained without enjoyment, although one was her favourite, orange cream. If she had been sharing them with a partner, they might have pretended to quarrel over it and ended up sharing it with a kiss. She laughed aloud at her romantic fancies, but the sound in the silent, silent house frightened her.

When the telephone rang, she stumbled over the dark room to seize the vibrating receiver and as she did so, reached out with her other hand and pressed the light switch. The room sprang into life in all its faded, familiar femininity.

"There now," she soothed the caller. "Don't worry. I'll see you in a wee while." And she managed a reassuring laugh.

"Oh it's all right for you to laugh, nurse," the patient said rather resentfully. "It's well seen you don't have a family. It's then you know what it is to suffer. But och, you're not the worst."

179

That's all very well, Nurse O'Hare thought, but it wasn't enough to be "not the worst." She would probably not hear from Hugh Fitzpatrick again.

But the next day, a box of chocolates was delivered to her by hand from the man himself, with the all too familiar words, "Just a wee minding, nurse."

Well he could keep them! "No, no, I was only doing my job," she said loftily instead of laughing with apparent pleasure as she usually did on receipt of a minding. But he lingered on her step and felt himself blushing, as he hadn't done since he was a callow boy.

"I'll send you flowers too," he said recklessly. "But please take these for now, they're Belgian."

She deigned to smile. "My favourites," she said, "and my name is Maeve. Have you time to come in?"

He did. It was the first of many visits and wee mindings. One of which was a sparkling engagement ring and Hugh was happy to tell all his cronies that she was not the worst but the best thing that ever happened to him.

To keep smiling had sometimes been difficult for Nurse O'Hare, but it came easily to Maeve Fitzpatrick.

BABY AND THE GOOSE

A MEMORY BY HILDA MCHUGH

Kilkishen, Co. Clare

After being bullied by a goose, Baby seeks out his revenge.

I t was a fight to the death. Let there be no doubt about this; pooh pooh to your lily livered theories of accident, lucky break, chance in a million or misadventure etc. This was quite simply an exquisitely planned deliberate execution.

The goose was pampered all her life, petted and patted by adults and fed tasty tidbits by everyone in sight. You would have thought that this treatment might have sweetened her nature somewhat. Not a hope of it; she was born mean-spirited, small-minded, pea-brained and egotistical and would die that way sooner rather than later if Baby had his way. Baby on the other hand was a softie, 20 months of burbling smiles, pudgy hands, angelic blond curls and laughing enthusiasm. But he had a well-developed terror of geese. Ganders chased him hissing vituperatively and unmercifully in every farmyard. Geese pecked savagely at his rosy and shiny cheeks and when they massed together to make a concerted attack on him, his terror knew no bounds. He knew that when they knocked him face down in their filthy droppings that they actually laughed at him, each his or her own individual derisive evil cackle reaching a cacophony of manic horror. Baby had his reasons. All he needed now was opportunity and timing and Heaven had just handed him both on a silver platter.

The goose had been fattened in the garden over the past months. She had her very own run in his garden; she had commandeered half of his play space and the adults had actually fenced it off as her terrain. Here she lorded it over all entrants to the garden, sidelining him and the other children without a by your leave or a single sympathetic thought. One of the older boys

181

had slyly suggested that maybe the goose's days were numbered and she might yet get her comeuppance at Christmas.

Baby had motive, he knew it was only a matter of waiting for the optimum opportunity. Then Mother did something unusual; she transferred the goose to new living quarters, the small toilet behind the kitchen door opening on to the back hall. This room was a last-minute inspirational change to the house plans by our Dad who worked shift duties involving three nights, three mornings and three evenings. He needed to be able to sleep during the day on a regular basis. At a very late stage in the building process it dawned on him that five children less than six years of age and an expectant wife living in a house with one upstairs bathroom next door to his bedroom, was hardly conducive to harmony, quietness or daytime rest. So what had been originally designed as a scullery was hastily fitted out as a downstairs toilet.

This then was to become the goose's quarters for the five days prior to Christmas. All the children were warned that this area was off limits and was to be kept under lock and key. For the next couple of days Mother carefully locked and unlocked the door if she needed to retrieve anything from the room or check on the goose. Unknown to her all her movements were being monitored by Baby. When on the third morning she emerged with a large saucepan she seldom used, which she usually stored on the top shelf, she forgot to turn the key in the lock.

Baby knew his moment had finally arrived. He waited until Mother was busy hanging out washing and then like the well-oiled commando machine he fancied himself to be, Baby made his move. Quick as a flash, silent and deadly he crept to the door, opened it a crack and waited for the narrow-skulled, evil head to appear. Then with all the force he was capable of, Baby grabbed the nipple end of his 8 oz. Pyrex bottle and *wham*, smacked the unsuspecting goose on top of the head between the eyes, killing it stone dead with one well-timed swoop. He then swiftly closed the door, restored the nipple to its rightful place and jauntily strutted towards Mother at the clothesline.

It may have been the glint of glee in his eye or perhaps the swagger that aroused Mother's suspicions because straight away, she rushed in to check on her precious goose. At first she thought the goose might only be stunned and all was not lost but eventually, she had to admit that the goose was indeed dead, killed by one fatal blow from a baby's bottle three days too early for Christmas.

LIFE AND THE FARM

By PHIL FEENEY
Carricmacross, Co. Monaghan

A woman fondly remembers her time spent on her aunt's farm as a child in Co. Monaghan.

It was the springtime of my life and my earliest memory. It was my Aunt Kathleen and about life on a small Monaghan farm. I was five years old. Kathleen lived on the farm with my grandparents, my four uncles and a grand collection of animals. They had cows, calves, pigs, working horses and a pony. The pony and trap took the family to mass on Sundays and the working horses brought back hay from the summer harvest and potatoes from the September-picking. Kathleen kept geese, turkeys, hens and strange chickens called guinea fowl. They laid their eggs anywhere and everywhere except in the areas they were supposed to. It was our job, as children, to find the hidden nests before the guinea hens hatched their eggs and arrived back with their little families of chicks.

Kathleen was in essence my second "Mother". My own Mother had six children in the space of eight years. I was the eldest; a girl and five boys arrived after me. I was always sent out to the farm when the new baby was coming. For a long time I thought my aunt had something to do with the baby but didn't know quite what it was. Every time I came back home to the town, there was a new baby brother waiting for me.

Over the years, Kathleen taught me how to churn and make butter from milk. She taught me how to make bread and how to cook it in a flat pot on the open fire with hot turf on the lid. The children always fought over who would get to blow the bellows and make the fire burn brighter.

Making jam was another wonderful skill she taught me. We had to pull all the fruit in season, prepare it and wash the jam jars. Kathleen always told us when we were pulling gooseberries and blackcurrants that we had to whistle in order to pick the best fruit. It was only years later when I realised the whistling was to prevent us eating all the fruit.

The children were always assigned to collect the eggs from the hens, ducks and guinea hens on a Wednesday night. We would wash and clean the eggs and leave them ready in a basket. Next morning my grandfather would get the pony and trap ready. We would load up the eggs and then head off for the Thursday Market in Carrickmacross. When my grandmother sold the eggs, we were rewarded with a large glass of Mi Wadi. That was a real treat.

When my uncles were cutting the hay, barley and wheat in the fields away from the farm, we would take the food and refreshments to them on our bikes. We too shared in the picnic, sitting on a bale of hay and joining in the "craic" of the day. The tea and sandwiches always tasted so good after hard work or a three mile cycle. We would always finish off the tea with Kathleen's currant bread, spread thickly with butter and homemade jam. The day of the "thrashing" was an especially busy day on the farm as all the meitheal would arrive to help. We had to prepare and present dinner and tea for near to 20 people. We borrowed tables and chairs from the neighbours, as they did from us on their harvest days and it was the children who served up the meals. When the meals ended, the washing up had to be done and that meant going to the well with our buckets for water. This was Ireland of the late 1940s and early 1950s.

There was one job everyone tried to avoid on the farm: the washing and sterilizing of the milk "separator". This was a machine for separating the cream from the milk. There were 40 different pieces to this machine to be washed, scrubbed and dried. It was used every single day, so that meant many trips to and from the well.

Another thing we dreaded on the farm, was getting a cut, graze or injury of any kind. Kathleen had a "cure all" in the form of a small bottle of Iodine kept on the top shelf of the dresser. We would quiver when we saw her reach up for that bottle, smile and slowly take the cork out of the bottle. The Iodine solution wasn't just for people: animals got it too. Baby chicks received this cure when they had the "Pip" - a type of chicken hiccup. Kathleen would get a long feather, dip it in the bottle and then nudge it down the chicken's throat. It worked every time.

My aunt was fully nestled into country life, life itself and the ever changing nature of the Irish seasons. In late January she gathered rushes from the bog, to make St. Brigid crosses. Brigid was always revered in Ireland. She was reputed to be the first Irish saint to have come through the transition from Celtic paganism to Christianity. Elements of paganism survived for more than 100 years after Christianity became firmly established in Ireland. Kathleen would tell us exactly where to go in the bog to get the best rushes. She made the first few crosses and then encouraged us to make them.

The crosses were distributed among the families and neighbours and were then blessed on February 1st - St. Brigid's Feast Day. Throughout homes all over Ireland, the cross would hang in a place of honour over the door, to ensure a rich harvest from Mother Nature until the next year.

The next custom was the Blessing of the Palms in Holy Week. At Easter, Kathleen supplied all the family with palm branches and when blessed on Palm Sunday, they were hung up in the house too. After Easter Sunday, we would bring our bottles to church and bring home fresh Holy Water. Homes, barns, fields, crops and animals were all blessed with the Easter Holy Water. On Easter Sunday afternoon, after the fasting of Lent, we were allowed to gather brosna (firewood) and make a fire out in the field at the back of the house. There, we would cook our Easter eggs in a big pot. All children were encouraged to put a mark of some sort on their own egg and many a time there was a squabble about whose egg you took out of the pot, how cooked it was or how hard or soft it was. Aunt Kathleen would bring out tea in a bottle, and some Siminel cake she had made especially for Easter. This picnic was called "An Cludog".

May time was very special on the farm as everything moved towards full bloom. On the eve of May, we would gather May flowers, buttercups and cowslips (all yellow in colour) in huge bunches and my grandmother and Aunt Kathleen would erect a May bush in front of the hall door and decorate it with the yellow flowers. They also put flowers on the roof and doorstep of the sheds and barn.

This was to welcome summer and ward off evil spirits. For the month of May, we would make an altar to Our Lady and keep fresh flowers on it every day. In the evening, about 9 pm we would all kneel and say the Rosary. The Rosary itself was fine but granny and Kathleen seemed to pray for everyone in the whole world and to us it seemed to go on forever. Sometimes the grandfather clock in the corner would strike 10 o'clock before we finished and got up off our knees.

When it came to growing vegetables and flowers, my aunt was in her own little heaven on earth. She would go to the bog and draw loads of rich black bog earth to put in the garden and pots. Her onions, lettuce radishes, scallions, beetroot, carrots, parsnips and cabbage were superb and in season she grew peas, broad and runner beans. There were no sprays, pesticides or chemicals used. Everything was natural and came from the animals and fowl manure. She would sow tomato seeds and when they started to grow, they would be transferred to the window sill inside, to get the benefit of the sun. We would have fresh tomatoes the whole summer long.

Every May, we would have the Procession of the Blessed Sacrament through the streets of Carrickmacross and the relations in the town depended on Aunt Kathleen to supply them with flowers to decorate their windows and doorways. She never failed them. She always provided the most beautiful wild flowers. She also walked in the procession wearing her Child of Mary Cloak. When I was 14, I received my own cloak. It was made of baby blue satin, without sleeves and knee length.

At Christmas time, Kathleen brought holly laden with red berries, plus a large black/grey turkey to my mother that she had reared herself. It was already fattened, killed, plucked, cleaned and dressed, ready for the oven. All my mother had to do was to make the stuffing and my aunt even supplied the thyme, parsley, sage and onions for this. St. Stephen's Day was magical on the farm, as there was always a party with lots of food, fruit and sweets, not forgetting the Christmas cake and pudding. We, the children, were allowed stay up late and watch the grown ups play cards and fight over a halfpenny here, a halfpenny there, or argue if someone didn't take a trick at the "right" time. Happy times, with the turf fire glowing and the oil lamp burning brightly and not a care in the world.

Years passed in idyllic bliss with most of my happiest memories surrounding my times with Kathleen and the farm. I fell in love, married as a teenager and moved to England to a totally different city life. Life was good but very different and I tried to maintain all the wisdom and simplicity of life I had gained from Kathleen. My husband, Jim and I had three children and we always looked forward to the summer holidays to return to Ireland and spend some time unwinding on the farm. My children loved the farm too, almost as much as I did and still do.

I remember the boys loved to play in the sawdust up at the "Sawing block" where sticks were prepared for the fire which burned all year round. Our boys would run their cars in the sawdust and make roads and towns and little stories in the dust. One day a large pig strolled up to where the boys were playing and calmly ate one of their cars.

My son roared, "Mum, Kathleen's hippo has eaten my car." The pig had been rolling in the duck pond and was quite dirty. These "city boys" had never seen a well soiled sow before, but they had seen a hippopotamus in the zoo. I was a little upset that my son had lost his toy but Kathleen was more concerned for the sow. There followed a few very anxious days. The pig was given some Castor oil and survived with no ill effects to its health. The children learned that farm animals, like people, had to be respected.

Years passed and in the 1970s, we came back to Ireland to set up home here once again. The children quickly blended in to the Irish life and schools and at the weekends, could hardly wait to get out to the farm to feed the hens, gather their eggs and generally be around their Gran Auntie Kathleen. She was always so full of life. By this time, my grandparents and my uncles had gone to their reward in heaven and Kathleen was alone on the farm. Her health then started to fail. Doctors had diagnosed her with Parkinson's Disease. The whole family all helped to look after her, to cook for her, to feed her and help her in every way they could. It was just as she had done for the whole family over the many years of our beautiful relationship. She was honoured with letters and medals from President Mary McAleese on the occasion of her 100th and 101st birthdays.

My Aunt Kathleen passed away peacefully on January 25th 2011. It was her 102nd year but the wisdom, simplicity and truth she gave to me and to my life, remain timeless.

Nylon Saga

A *memory by* Rose Kelleher

A young girl has a mishap with her aunt's nylon stockings.

I was raised on a small farm in Co. Monaghan in the early '40s. Being the eldest of a family of 10, I had to help picking potatoes, cutting turf, pulling flax and milking cows by hand. Many of these chores had to be done before school. Electricity hadn't been connected until the late '50s.

Our farm bordered Aunt Maura's farm. She inherited it as she was the youngest in her family of 13. Aunt Maura, my Mum's youngest sister, was a school teacher blessed with beauty, brains and a charming personality. She was renowned for helping the poor and disadvantaged at home and abroad. She would elicit help from the neighbours, local farmers and pupils to sell tickets for her various charitable enterprises. Dad was always nabbed to spin the "Wheel of Fortune" and the local police sergeant distributed the prizes.

Maura was a reckless driver and Dad would be hanging on for dear life when escorting her to the bank with the proceeds of the enterprises. Hens and ducks would scatter in every direction when her Morris Minor would whiz into our yard. She was the first lady in our neighbourhood to wear nylon stockings.

Nylon was the new wonder material back in the '30s. I often wonder if Wallace Carothers and his team of scientists hadn't been successful in the manufacturing of this synthetic material in Delaware, would I have a different story to tell?

My Mum was continuously baking and one of my weekly chores was to bring fresh brown bread and scones, wrapped in a white pillowcase, to Aunt Maura. I relished the loaf bread and jam she gave me as white bread was scarce then. It was a frosty evening in November, the moon bright in the sky, nothing to hear only the crackling of the frost under my wellingtons. When I arrived at Maura's, she shouted from upstairs to "throw on a few sods of turf on the fire and don't let it quench." I lifted the lid of her quaint Modern Mistress range and a blast of air suddenly sucked Maura's pink bloomers and her nylon stockings into the fire, singeing my ringlets in the process. Clothes were always aired on the overhead rack.

I was shocked, shaking and motionless. Oh, how could I tell her? I remember her telling Mum how she queued for two hours in Clery's to purchase them and they cost 29 shillings and 6 pence, half her week's salary. I ran across the fields looking over my shoulder every so often. I slipped in cow manure and a hare ran across my path, frightening the life out of me.

Mam was darning socks when I ran in the door. I tried to explain all that had happened. She listened attentively, her eyes and mouth opening wider. Squeezing me to her bosom, she advised to explain everything to Aunt Maura, every syllable getting softer and slower.

Filling the stone jar, she marched me to bed. "On your way home from Confession, you can call to Aunt Maura," she advised.

How could I tell Fr. Cooke what had happened? I was restless. I heard Mum regaling the episode to Dad.

"Where is the geirsha now?" he enquired.

"Poor soul must be asleep," she replied.

Fr. Cooke was entering the confessional. I ran into the box and blurted out, half crying, "I burned Aunt Maura's bloomers and nylons, Father." I was hoping Mrs. Brady couldn't hear me at the other side. I don't know if Fr. Cooke had a cold or was laughing but I had my three Hail Marys said in a jiffy.

I ran to Aunt Maura's house but the door was locked. Had she called to Mum to complain? There were butterflies in my tummy again. How long more would I have to wait and face the music?

It was almost a week later when I heard the sound of a car driving slowly into our yard. Maura wasn't driving. Out from the passenger seat this vision appeared, dressed like a queen. It was Aunt Maura - she was so happy and excited.

Mum, taking off her print apron and grabbing and putting my hand into Maura's, she said, "Some little girl has a story to tell you," and gave me a whimsical grin.

Just then, Paul hopped out of the car and extended his lovely soft hands as Maura introduced him to all of us. The glitter of her Solitaire ring almost dazzled us. I could have told Maura anything; she wasn't listening.

When I met her the next day, she said, "Lucky you didn't burn all your curls." Then, whispering in my ear she continued, "You'll be my flower girl at my wedding next Shrove Tuesday, please God."

That was the longest three months I ever waited. The memory of the nylon saga still haunts me 65 years on.

TIES THAT BIND

By ANN BENTLEY

Kildare Town

*An uncle receives some bad news about his niece whom he loves
dearly.*

H e knew there was something wrong when he saw how
her hand kept straying to her apron pocket as she sat
at the end of the table and she was up and down like
a yoyo, seeing to the fire, moving the kettle up onto the hob
and then off again. Anything to put off telling him what was
bothering her.

He'd seen the postman from the top of the field where he'd
been working and was waiting for her to say something. Now
he knew it had to be bad news.

"Well, what is it?" he demanded, pushing back his chair and
turning to face her.

"It's bad, Joe, not much hope," his mother answered.

His face pales. "Not much hope?" he said, "not much hope?
But she's just homesick!"

"She's in hospital, Joe. She's not responding to treatment."

Getting up from the table, he went to the mantlepiece over
the fireplace and took down the small tin box where any money
they had was kept. "I'm going to get her, bring her home," he
said, and walking out the door, he got his bicycle from the end
of the house and was halfway up the lane before she realised
what he was hoping to do.

She watched him cycle down the long laneway as she'd
watched all the others. She had let them all go. Worse, she had
to encourage them. How could she keep them buried here in the
bog with her? Nothing to look forward to, only hardship.

"Spread your wings," she said, "reach for the moon. Work,
study, make something of yourselves, but above all, be happy.
And remember you can always come home if you don't like it."

Joe had stayed at home, had eventually taken over the running of the place. She had pleaded with him many times to at least go and see what the outside world was like, visit his brothers and sisters abroad. He wouldn't even go for a holiday, had never been farther than the local market town ten miles away. The small farm was enough for him, working in the fields, around the farmyard, he was content. Now here he was cycling off to London to bring home Maeve's child.

Maeve, the child of her old age, old for childbearing at least, born when all the others were already making their own way in the world. Happy, laughing, trusting Maeve, spoiled by everyone, especially her doting father. Maybe it was a blessing God had taken him before she took up with that go-boy from the village. How could she ever think he would marry her? No job, no interest in working, he wouldn't even give a helping hand in his parents' grocery store. Nothing in him but good looks and a roving eye. It was better for all concerned when, at the mention of fatherhood, he had taken off to his brother in Australia.

"Bring the baby home," Nan said when Maeve broke the news to her. "Go to your sister in England for a while. She's always asking you. And you know the child will be all right here with me."

The gurgling, happy baby kept the old lady busy, but Joe hardly ever spoke to the child, did his best to ignore her.

"Bronwen," he'd said that first day, "Bronwen, what sort of a name is that?"

The child loved him from the first moment they met. Her eyes followed his every move and as soon as she could walk, she began to follow him everywhere. He kept telling his mother to "keep that half-door closed". He had enough to do; he hadn't time to be watching the child.

She was almost two when she crawled out under the fence he had climbed over and began to toddle after him across the bog field. He turned at his mother's call and saw the child. He strode back to pick her up and take her back across the field, but when she smiled into his angry face and tightened her chubby arms around his neck, his heart melted. He waved to his mother and walked off across the field with the child perched on his shoulders. They'd been almost inseparable ever since.

"Come, my little brown one," he'd say, "and we'll feed the cows, we'll plough the field, we'll turn the hay." He'd even taken her up the ladder to help mend the thatch. And once a week he'd sit her on the bar of his bike to take her to the village shop for a treat.

Maeve had found work in England. She wrote every week, often sent money and clothes and was always home for the summer holidays. It was on the child's third birthday that she told them she was taking the child to live with her, start her schooling over there. She had a good job, a nice flat with a good school nearby. Nan didn't want to remember that time. How Bronwen had clung to Joe, how the child had cried till she was so sick they had to put off the journey for two days. How Maeve had persuaded Joe to go as far as the shop with them and how they had driven off when he got out of the car to get her a treat. How he had hated deceiving the child. But, of course, it was for her own good.

He had moped about for weeks afterwards, spending long hours walking through the fields. Luckily there was plenty of work to keep him busy even if he didn't have the same interest in it anymore. He didn't seem to have much interest in anything except the letters.

"She's not settling in very well," Maeve wrote, "but of course it's a different way of life, she'll soon get used to it." But she didn't get used to it, she wasn't talking … she wouldn't eat … she's in hospital, and now "there's not much hope."

"Ted, I have to go to Dublin, the airport," Joe said leaning his bicycle against the low hedge behind which Ted Corrigan was working in his garden. Ted was the local unofficial taxi driver for the whole community, always ready to help especially when someone was in trouble. Sticking his spade in the ground, he looked at Joe.

"The child, is it?" he asked.

"She's bad, Ted," Joe said, nodding his head. "I'm going to get her, bring her home."

"I don't suppose you've booked a flight, have you?" Ted asked. "No? Well, never mind, we'll go to the airport, see if we can arrange something. You can't get a plane the way you can get a bus, you know."

Not that Joe had ever been on a bus. He walked or cycled anywhere he had to go. If there were a few turkeys, pigs, calves or anything else his mother might need a helping hand with selling at the local market, he'd load up the pony and cart for her, meet her in the town and cycle home again as soon as the selling was done. Ted, now retired, had travelled widely and had worked abroad for many years, so finding his way around the airport was no trouble to him. He didn't think there was much chance of Joe getting a flight that evening but he knew it was no use trying to tell him that. Better go to the airport with him and hope for a little miracle.

It took quite a while, but eventually Joe was on the four o' clock flight to London. He had insisted on booking a return flight for later that night. Ted didn't hold out much hope for him getting back that night but eventually Joe agreed to make the booking for 10.30 instead of the eight o'clock which Joe was hoping for. Ted started to drive home, but changed his mind. He'd hang around for a while, visit friends, be back at the airport to meet the eight o'clock flight from London as well as the 10.30. Or any other flight that Joe might be on that night.

It was almost six o'clock when Joe arrived at the hospital. He had ignored the strange looks he'd been getting as he tried to find out where to get a taxi, but he supposed he did look a sight in his working clothes and hobnail boots. Now the taxi was waiting outside the hospital for him. The group around the bed looked up as he made his way over to them, then seeing the look on his face, they parted to let him through. Sitting down on the side of the bed, he looked down at the shadow of the child he had known. Gently, he touched her curls, laid his hand on her cheek, then carefully he lifted her up in his arms whispering,

"Bronwen, my little brown one, I've come to take you home. There's a car outside waiting to take us to a lovely big aeroplane that will take us to Dublin where we can get on the bus to Kildare. Your granny has the bed all ready for you and you'll never have to go away again. I'm taking her home, sis," he said, glancing over at his sister as he stood up and started to walk to the door. Speechless, she watched, then nodded her head.

A nurse tucked a blanket around the child. "Don't let her get cold," she warned as he walked out of the ward. Back at London Airport after much to-ing and fro-ing and a very helpful airport attendant, he was finally boarding the eight o'clock plane for Dublin.

He talked almost non-stop to the child. In the taxi, at the airport, on the plane. He told her how Speedy and Racer, the old plough horses, looked up expectantly every time he came near, then hung their heads in disappointment when she wasn't there to sing "horsey, horsey do not stop" to them. How Ruadh, the old red cow, looked all round at milking time wondering why there were no little soft hands to pat her side.

"And Quacky," he said, "goes quacking round and round the yard looking in every hole and corner as if she's trying to ask 'where's Bronwen?' She has a brood of lovely fluffy ducklings she wants to show you. And poor little Rascal is nearly worn out from barking and running up and down the car-road wondering where you've gone. Old Mutt won't budge from the top gate watching for you to come home."

"And, of course, your Gran' misses you. She says, 'the house is too lonely without you and there's no one to help her with the baking and the churning, or with feeding the chickens or bringing in the turf, and there's no one to sit beside her when she goes to town in the pony and cart. And, of course, you haven't forgotten Tiger, your own special cat, have you? She has the loveliest little kitten you've ever seen. We've been racking our brains trying to think of a name for her, but we can't decide on anything. I suppose we don't really want to as Tiger is your cat, Bronwen, so you should name her kitten. She doesn't look a bit like Tiger, no stripes at all, just a lovely creamy-white fur, almost the colour of your Gran's best coat. You know that nice bainin one she wears on special occasions?"

"Bainin. We'll call her Bainin," he heard a small voice whisper, or was it just wishful thinking? Looking down at the child in his arms, he saw dark eyes, too big for the small pinched face, open briefly and a faint smile touch the pale lips.

"Bronwen, my own little brown one," he said, as the tears ran unheeded down his weather-beaten cheeks and the lump in his throat felt as if it would choke him. "You're going to be all right; everything's going to be all right now."

The Mother, the Ingrate and the Piano

By Maggie Beggan
Clonshaugh, Dublin

When Mother decides to sell an old piano, her daughter has mixed feelings about its departure.

O n a cold dark night in 1989, I made my way up Cricklewood Broadway to the telephone box and anxiously dialled the number.

"Hello, Mother?" I said cautiously. I'd been summoned to ring her tonight at an appointed time and was killed wondering what Mother wanted that was so urgent. What it was that couldn't be said in the letters that I received almost daily from her. The Mother wrote to me religiously every day, letters in her telltale almost incomprehensible scrawl, looping and diving regardless of the pre-printed lines designed to keep the characters on the right track. Letters written at the old kitchen table at home, between the morning news which kept her always sharp mind abreast of all things current, politically and otherwise, and The Gay Byrne Radio Show, which like all of her peers of a certain age, she couldn't go without listening to.

"It was a bit of skit," she said and you'd hear all sorts of interesting items on it. She'd go on to declare that he was "the consumer's champion". No matter what the injustice perpetrated on the humblest person, the mere threat of writing to Gay Byrne was enough to get you your money back or have it settled to your satisfaction forthwith! He was also a great man for playing the old tunes that she loved so much.

The moment I saw the Mother smile and the tea-towel that seemed always to be in her hand, flick up and over her shoulder, I knew that I would be dragged from my seat to be the Mother's partner for this dance around the kitchenette. I always enjoyed our waltzing and quickstepping, it was fun, until I got older and it was embarrassing, though there was no one there to ridicule me. I do the same thing now with my own children, sweep them up in my arms and twirl them around the room to the strains of a favourite melody in the background and see their little faces full of joy, head thrown back and mouth open with laughter as I spin round and round. They never want it to end and I suppose I didn't either, one time.

Staring at the receiver in my hand I was apprehensive too, for the Mother was in the habit of sending me articles from the newspapers at home about how well all the young Irish people were doing for themselves in London and regaling me with tales of various cousins and neighbours who were sprinting up the corporate ladder – globally! It was supposed to encourage not to criticise, but it didn't seem that way to me at the time. I was her youngest and felt that all her hopes were pinned on me. I was bound to fail under the expectation. Sure, through my distorted immature view of life, that I would make a bags of it. She always harboured high hopes for all her children but our ambition just wasn't there, despite her best efforts. The Mother shouldered part of the blame for her offspring's underachievement fair and square, when she announced cynically in her mid 50s that it got you nowhere in life being honest and hardworking. And so, she set about the vain attempt to unravel all the values she herself had instilled so soundly in her children.

"It's no use being humble and meek," she insisted. "You'll be treated like a doormat!" Her deconstruction of the tenets she'd taught us proved an impossible task and I'm glad now that it was one of the Mother's failed experiments, like so many others. We all turned out decent, well-liked people who inherited her charm and our father's wit and we are a credit to her – retrospectively! But she always hoped for the very best for us and always strived desperately to help our financial fate along through her madcap entrepreneurial endeavours which took many forms over the years. The focus and drive behind them when it was my turn, was to get me trained and into the classical piano scene no less!

"Don't set your sights too high, Mother," I said.

"Oh I won't, love," she yelled from the top of the Empire State Building. Metaphorically, of course!

"I'm selling the piano, pet; it's taking up too much room." So there it was. The reason for the call. Surprisingly, I was stunned. Why? I didn't know. The damn thing was the bane of my childhood and I hated it with all my heart. But it was part of my childhood and my home too – despite the fact that in the last few years it had become the dumping ground for every piece of domestic flotsam and jetsam imaginable. It's a wonder no-one was killed in an avalanche sitting under it! And no matter where you sat, there it was mockingly taking up half the kitchen in our corporation house.

"How do you feel about that?" the Mother continued, "if you've any intention of taking it up again I'll keep it, but to be honest, love, I need the money and a bit of space too." It was the words I'd longed to hear for years and yet I was hurt and confused and angry all at once. It was a dastardly curse about to be lifted, a reminder of my many failings about to be banished, but I didn't feel happy.

"Sell it if you want to," I said a little too curtly. "What do I care? The way it is if I want to take it up again I can buy meself one!" It's a wonder I didn't add, "So there! Nah nah nee nah nah" and blow a raspberry too for good measure! I was an adult, 21 years of life experience under my belt, the big cheese.

The Mother said she was sorry but needs must, and it made no sense to keep it if I wasn't coming home again or going to teach piano as she had always hoped for. The Mother resisted getting the dig in too blatantly about all the sacrifices that were made for that blasted piece of furniture and all the time we spent in screaming matches and bad humours when I was forced to practice an hour a day, day in - day out for years on end. I'd be pounding away on the scales and the arpeggios and all the kids of the nation would be screeching and frolicking and having the best fun ever right outside the window, not a care in the world did any of them have. I envied them. The day I came home at age five with the note from teacher about piano lessons was the beginning of the end of a carefree childhood. The Mother thought it would be a marvellous privilege to be able to pay for lessons for me. Her sons were all musicians, self-taught, and she was delighted that her financial situation had improved over the years to the extent that she could pay for proper lessons for the spoiled crab of the family. My older sister had gotten an earlier glimpse of the gravy train too but escaped my fate by somehow picking a violin teacher who plunged to his death down the stairs at his home, breaking his neck in the fall. My sister was understandably put off the whole idea then and that was the end of her musical apprenticeship. I was not so lucky.

The night of the phone call, lying in my lonely bed in London I thought about all the trouble that piano had caused. How the Mother, in trying to enrich my life and give me opportunities for my future that she or my siblings would never know, had driven a wedge between us. She'd race me to lessons once a week to a renowned teacher, an Anglo-Irish aristocratic eccentric who insisted on being remunerated monthly in guineas and addressed as "Madame"! She would beat my knuckles with a stick from the comfort of her chair at the other end of her "studio".

On Wednesdays, the Mother would screech to a halt outside the primary school in her battered Renault 4, the door would swing open and I'd hop in. We were always running late for the Madame. The Mother would have my dinner on a plate with a saucepan lid on top, wrapped in a tea cloth to keep it warm, a knife and fork and a bottle of brown sauce on the dashboard. Meat and two veg, cooked like every other meal, in her revolutionary pressure cooker that filled the house with condensation that ran down the walls and windows and made everything taste like turnip. What must we have looked like, tearing through Rialto and me eating my dinner? Meals on wheels took on a whole new meaning!

The cost of the piano, the lessons, the exams and the sheet music alone over the many years of battle, especially after she was made a widow, was beyond my concern, but looking back it must have cost a huge amount of sacrifice. The Mother, always ahead of her time, had many cunning money making schemes, like delivering leaflets and newspapers, cleaning houses and offices, home hairdressing and once even the assembly of funeral wreaths consisting of imitation carnations under plastic domes. This particular venture was on a strictly "need to know" basis and went on clandestinely in the back bedroom of our small corporation house, until the Father stumbled by chance on the macabre cottage industry and after roaring, "Holy heart of Jaysus!", shut down the whole operation.

The ultimate sale of the piano ironically provided the Mother with the only joy or pleasure ever extracted from it when the man who answered the small ad put it through its paces and he and the Mother spent an evening around it, belting out all the old songs and had a right auld impromptu hooley. It was what she had always hoped for from the old hunk of wood all along.

The Mother died suddenly and prematurely the following spring and that was that. In the many years that have passed since then, I have proudly stated that I am a graduate of the Royal Irish Academy of Music and a classically trained pianist. Technically true, but in reality I can't read or play a note any more and never did take it up again.

Her old adage oft' repeated that "Mother knows best" proved true, but I thought I knew better.